William

PERHAPS I AM

PERHAPS I AM

BY
EDWARD W. BOK

AUTHOR OF "THE AMERICANIZATION OF EDWARD BOK," "TWO PERSONS,"
"A MAN FROM MAINE," "TWICE THIRTY"
EDITOR OF "GREAT HOLLANDERS"

CHARLES SCRIBNER'S SONS
NEW YORK · LONDON
1928

TO

CATHERINE NORNABELL

IN GRATEFUL RECOGNITION OF HER PART
IN THE PRODUCTION OF THIS BOOK.

I am Retired Leisure. I am to be met with in trim gardens. I am already come to be known by my vacant face and careless gesture, perambulating at no fixed pace, nor with any settled purpose. I walk about: not to and fro.

CHARLES LAMB.

THERE should be the names of two authors to this book, but I have not been able to convince the other author that his name should accompany mine on the title-page.

The story of it is this:

A successful merchant was beguiled by his wife to read my book *Twice Thirty*. The book gripped him, and he decided that the time had come in his business life to retire. He did retire. His wife then convinced him that before he undertook something in the way of service he should first take a vacation to counteract the physical wear and mental tear of the years of business life, see what the world was doing, and stretch the walls of his mind. This he did for his first year of freedom. At the end of that time his wife induced him to write a book. But after he had done so he realized that book-writing was not his forte. So he sent the manuscript to me, asking if I would read it and "touch it up here and there" where needed in order to make a book, which he said he realized he had failed to do.

It did not take me long to discover that he had readable material in his book. He had observed well, and selected his experience even better. But, like many another man, he had not the ability to tell other people what he had seen or experienced. His incidents had become almost lost in a sea of words. I saw that to "touch it up here and there" really meant to re-write the entire book. This I did, leaving the incidents and facts absolutely alone, but changing their presentation to the reader. I sent him the result, and he was highly satisfied. The facts were still his, but the method of telling them had changed—he thought much for the better.

That he had selected the most interesting experiences: had collected readable facts—surprising in some instances—there was no doubt. They simply needed a genial, readable presentation. It would be a pity, I thought, if such a readable collection of experiences and incidents did not reach the public. I then suggested to him that his name appear with mine on the title-page. To this he returned with: "No, that would not be fair. Had the original book gone out it was my idea not to use my name as author: I had already selected a pseudonym. Now, I cannot find myself anywhere in the book: hence my identification with the changed result would not be fair. The book is now wholly yours: the responsibility is yours, just as is my retirement from business yours. But for your book I never would have thought of retiring. You are doubly responsible."

But am I?

There is still a question here.

However, perhaps I am.

Edward W. Bok

AN INTRODUCTORY WORD

IT is fifteen months ago, as I write, that I was reading, one evening, that little wizard of financial truth
and economic wisdom, the *National City Bulletin*. My
"Wall Street Bible," my wife calls it. I was trying
to figure out the investment of some imminent divi-
dends. I was pretty deep in my calculations when I
heard my wife close a book she had been reading, with
a bang, and exclaim: "There, that is what I call a
book."

"Yes," I muttered mechanically. "Good."

"Just then came a whiff of sachet, my wife was
perched on the arm of my chair, my precious "Wall
Street Bible" was gently but firmly taken out of my
hand and a book put therein.

"You must read it," was the injunction.

"Yes?" I queried as I looked longingly at the *Bulletin* in my wife's hands, and with much less interest
at the book. Then a glance at the title of the book.
It was Edward W. Bok's *Twice Thirty*. "Oh, yes,"
I commented.

"He has you in it," said my wife.

"Has me in it?" I echoed. "Nonsense, woman."

"But he has, just the same," was the assurance.

Adroit woman that!

"I'm going up-stairs now, dear," she continued. "You begin it—and find yourself," was the parting word.

Of course, I began it! I was in a book! Couldn't figure out how that could be!

Next morning, at breakfast, My Lady asked: "Did you begin *Twice Thirty?*"

"Finished it!" I returned. "At four this morning."

"Did you find yourself?" came next.

"I did"—laconically.

"Well," she returned with a smiling face, "don't you think, as the advertisement says: 'It's time to retire'?"

"What?" I asked in amazement. "I retire? You mean——"

"I thought you said you found yourself in the book," was the neat shot.

"But, my dear——" I began.

"Now, dear, listen. Your digestion is all upset now and you can't live without bicarbonate of soda. You are headed for a crabbed old age, full of indigestion pains. Now, why? We have enough and to spare. Why go on worrying yourself? Be sensible."

Every husband understands, I think. A husband can struggle and wriggle all he likes. But a thing only works one way when your wife sets her mind on it. Particularly when you know inwardly—although loath to acknowledge it—that it is for your good.

So this worked out.

The next day my attention was called to an advertisement: "Eventually: Why Not Now?"

And eventually became now in this case. Within two months I had said good-by to my company—reserving a financial interest, but actively out. The Vice-President sits at my desk, and I am out—except from the Board.

It was a break, of course. The idea of a lifetime had fastened itself upon me: every day at the desk except when I was on the links. No vacation in eight years, because the summer time was our heyday when building was on. We were in cement. Then, of course, the usual thought: How would the company get on without my services? How about my obligations to the stockholders? All that. But it was wonderful how things ironed themselves out, with a distinct goal in sight. The way simply opened up. The whole thing began to seem more and more right.

Then? Couldn't keep away from the first four Board meetings. As new deals and new ideas came before the meetings, of which I was not and would not be an active part, I felt perfectly willing and content to miss the next two. The company was doing a larger business than ever. It was a tug at Pride— at first, naturally. Couldn't quite make it out. But there were the figures. Younger men were in the saddle, and each on the tips of his toes. They were as I had been fifteen years before.

Now? I have had a wonderful year and a quarter: wonderful. I never realized how interesting the world was outside of cement. Never gave myself time to look around and find out. True, that is all I have done so far: getting acquainted with currents that I never knew were running and eddying through Life, with persons and interests I never knew existed. Fascinating. Of course, there is more to the great world of things than this, and I intend from now on to get into them. But my wife was right when she counselled: "Take a year to find yourself and see what is what and who's who in the world. Your time now is for readjustment."

So here I am on the threshold, as it were, of what? I don't know. But interesting years. That I can already sense.

True, I have fallen down on the first thing I attempted outside of my work: writing this book. But how could I be expected to write a book? Never had any experience, and you cannot transform a cement manufacturer into an author within a year. But I am glad, in a sense, that I did fail. Never, for one minute, could I have written as it now stands. Everywhere in the pages which follow is the trained hand, and I confess I read it through at one sitting with true delight.

So, while I failed in one sense, in another I have succeeded in giving to the public a readable, interesting book.

I am satisfied, and I hope the public may be.

CONTENTS

PART I

PART II

xvii

PART III

PART I

CHAPTER ONE

THE FIRST LITTLE LADY IN THE LAND

In which I begin to tell what I found out when, in the first year of my freedom from business, I began to stop, look, and listen.

CHAPTER ONE
THE FIRST LITTLE LADY IN THE LAND

I

A DAY with nothing to do!

It was really a grand and glorious feeling! It was on the morning of the day after I left the corporation. I awakened to face a day with not an engagement in it. I had overslept from the strenuous day before. I lay for half an hour with the thought, and then deliberately took a full hour to dress.

"Always wanted an hour to dress," I said to The Lady of the Home when she came in to see if I "were alive." "Now I can take it."

At the breakfast-table no need to rush through the paper leading to a marathon to the office. "I can read the paper after breakfast," I explained.

"A splendid beginning," came from The Lady. "A courteous one, too. A wife is never complimented by a husband behind a newspaper at the breakfast-table. What's your programme for the day?"

"The newspaper after breakfast for an hour," I said. "Then the first act in my career of freedom is to slip round to Daughter's to see the baby. I haven't

5

seen as much of that granddaughter of mine as I liked."

"Good. I'll go with you."

II

We arrived at our daughter's home at a stormy time. The face of The Little Lady was red with offended dignity, and a torrential April shower was in progress. Everything was wrong in the baby-world. That was evident. And she so small, such a mite to set it all right. She felt so strongly that all things can be set right except everything.

III

"A stormy welcome," was my greeting from The Little Mother. "She is so unhappy: so deeply offended: everything is just plain wrong. We can do nothing with her."

And to verify The Little Mother's plaint, an entirely fresh deluge poured forth! The whole world was a vale of tears.

"Let me take her," said the grandmother.

But that did not avail.

"Suppose you let me try," I ventured humbly.

A united chortle came from mother and grandmother.

"You?" came the united chorus. "That is really funny, Daddy."

"Well, I crave to be funny," I humbly assented.

"Lovely," came once more the feminine chorus. "What can you do when, united, we can do nothing to get her quiet?"

"Can't do any worse than you two," I returned.

IV

And as the little bundle of pink and white soft wool, with a little soul inside, was laid in my arm, I thought I heard a little voice saying:

"Quiet? Well, I like that! What would you do if you were a girl with no hair and no clothes on, and couldn't talk and couldn't even stand, and your dignity was trampled on? Wouldn't you burst forth?"

I agreed heartily, and wondered how the little dignity had been so ruthlessly treated. Then came the explanation:

"They stick me in a sheet of water as big as the Atlantic Ocean and tell me to swim when I can't: they wrap me in a big towel so that I can't breathe: rub my eyes so that I can't see: jab a stick with cotton up my nose: a dry rag in my mouth: throw powder all over my body so that I nearly sneeze my head off: pin some horribly tight thing across my stomach, and then push a bit of rubber in my mouth. All in five minutes. There's no thought of my dignity or anything. How can a self-respecting woman keep quiet with such treatment, I ask you? I'll tell the world."

And she did!

I again agreed with her!

V

"Well, then, here goes once more" and— But it didn't go. Something happened. The little face grew red with offended dignity: the little brow creased, the mite of a chin puckered up, and all was ready for a perfect deluge, when— The eyes opened just a slit. The face grew calm. The storm signals gathered once more. But again the eyes opened,—a little wider. They couldn't open all the way because they were so very full of the April showers. Finally they did. They rested on the face looking down into them. For a moment they glanced. Then a steady look: a look of wonder. The little arms shot out, the body drew itself straight and struggled to get into an up-right position. The eyes now rested full on the face above them. A deep, heavy sigh shook the harassed body. Then with a look at the two women stand-ing by for corroboration, and as the eyes shifted once more to the face above, the words were almost audible:

"Well, where in the world did you come from? A man at that!"

Then seeing a large hand resting on the pink and white afghan, a little hand slowly reached forth and touched the large hand.

"Real, for a fact. Now, what do you know about that?"

Another sigh, very deep this time. Followed a steady look at the face above. Then a furtive look at the two cruel torturers standing by and a return look, with the thought almost expressed:

"Well, you look different, and you look safe. I think I can trust you not to let those cruel females get me."

VI

Then a look of the most interested discovery, the little hand reached up, two little fingers came through a button-hole, with a diminutive thumb outside, all clutching valiantly. The head turned to the black coat, another deep sigh and then: "I think I like that little dark corner right in there." And the little troubled face sought in that dark corner a haven where one's dignity would not be assailed and where the outraged are at rest. The little fingers loosened and slid through the button-hole and down the side of the coat, the little body relaxed,—and with a final look from half-opened eyes as if to say "Still there? Well, I'm off for a nap," the eyes closed.

The Little Lady had left this troubled world, and was asleep. Only a little twitching of the mouth reflected the terrible experience she had been through! The clock ticked the seconds into minutes and the minutes into the quarter, then into the half and into the full hour,—and still The Little Lady slept in utter and complete trust, with the little nose deep in the dark armor of her Saviour and Defender!

VII

So to Her, as she lay there, on the morning of my first day of freedom

THE FIRST LITTLE LADY IN THE LAND

to be my grandchild, sleeping so trustfully and peacefully in her grandfather's arm, safe from trampled dignity and outraged feelings

I Dedicate
This First Chapter

—quietly, very softly. For I would not disturb her for all the wealth in the world, even by the heart-beats which so fervently say: May Life be good to Her!

CHAPTER TWO
"IN THE WAY SHE SHOULD GO"

I am perfectly willing to leave the complete efficiency of this wise and simple mode of the training of a grand-daughter to any grandfather who may read these words.

CHAPTER TWO

"IN THE WAY SHE SHOULD GO"

I

I CANNOT understand the changed attitude of women toward me.

They approach me with the most sombre faces: they shake their heads in an ominous fashion: they go so far as to shake their fingers in my face until I expect any moment to be speared by their piano-finish finger-nails.

"Nice problem you are going to create for those dear young parents," says one.

"Pleasant child that is going to be to live with," says another.

"Model young lady that will be," flings a third.

"Poor parents. That's all I have to say," brings forth still another.

And all because I happened to casually remark that little girls were made so that their grandfathers could give them what they wanted whenever they wanted it!

One would imagine I had committed a crime in laying down that simple code of education. And when

I added to it, in a moment of glowing anticipation, that some day my granddaughter and I will start at 59th Street in New York, walk down Fifth Avenue and we will go into any store she likes and she shall buy whatever she wants, the feminine part of my audience simply shrieked as if in pain.

"A man's sole idea of making a woman happy," said one, with a really withering contempt.

"You would think we had not another idea in our heads than dress and baubles," added a second.

I noticed, however, that the little girl in my arm looked up at me, smiled, and cooed. She said it almost in words: "Don't mind them. They are unworthy members of my sex. You and I understand each other."

We do.

Any little granddaughter, even though she is only eight weeks old, can understand such grandfatherly love.

II

I wonder if women are jealous of the ability of grandfathers to train little granddaughters? If the mothers realize their shortcomings?

It may be, as Hamlin Garland once said, that only a father can train a daughter. Why should it not be equally true that only a grandfather understands the workings of a granddaughter's heart?

I wouldn't be at all surprised if that were it!

For it has been said, and wisely so, I think, that marriage is an institution created solely for the rejuvenation of grandfathers!

CHAPTER THREE

"JUST TALK ON PAPER"

"Now, don't try to write. You talk well, and tell a story well. Just talk on paper, and tell very simply just what you have observed, heard, and found out during your first year of freedom. Don't try for a connected story: just ramble along with incident, anecdote, and observation. If something suggests an experience of the past, put it in," counselled The Lady.

That was the starting gun.

Really unnecessary, for just to talk on paper is all that I thought I could do, I not having written a line for print, except for trade papers, since my senior year at college.

But all this was not so easy as it sounded: "talk on paper"— And it so proved, for after it was done I realized I had talked too much: and that the point I wanted to make was lost in a sea of words. After all, this was not surprising. A merchant cannot be transformed into an author in a year. So, after all, I had to turn the book over to another hand, and now I am glad I did.

CHAPTER THREE
"JUST TALK ON PAPER"

I

THERE seemed only one fly in the ointment when I stepped aside to sit on the fence for a while. I was made conscious that I had driven the old machine pretty hard for the years past, and the digestive apparatus didn't work any too well.

"That is first," laid down The Lady. "Get well. You can't look or listen or enjoy if you must have your mind on bicarbonate of soda half the time. Have Doctor Thornton look you over. Blood pressure, heart-beats and all that. But particularly your digestion. Then we'll talk of doing things, going places, seeing folk, and so on."

"You're all right, except that you're all wrong," said the cheerful M. D. "All screwed up. Back as tight as a drum. Nervous tension. What you need is to let go. Relax. Rest."

"How, specifically?" I asked.

"Well, before dinner every evening take a quiet hour and absolutely rest. Let go. Cultivate a perfectly blank mind. Do nothing. And drop your jaw."

"Drop my jaw?" I echoed.

"So!" and he demonstrated. "The theory is that while really we have no nerve centre, the jaw comes nearest to it. Relax the jaw, and almost every nerve relaxes. Try it. You won't look handsome in the act. But it will relieve tension, and with no tension your normal digestion will come back. Meanwhile eat lightly of certain things, and nothing of most things. I'll give you a diet list."

I began next day. I went The Man of Medicine one better by having (unknown to him) an osteopathic treatment directly after the quiet session with my jaw, then a tub, and dinner.

II

I got to like that hour! I had to acknowledge the efficacy of it. I had never before aspired to think hours into moments. An open hour had meant an opportunity too golden to lose. Something had to be started. But I had met a new experience. I had started to think only to find myself dreaming, then simply just sitting and with the mind an absolute blank. I had never had a state of mind before that would stay absolutely blank. The experience was interesting. It sounds stupid, but I didn't find it so when I began to get results. I began to feel differently, my digestion began to improve, and when I went in to dinner I was greeted by The Lady of the

Home and friends: "You are getting to look like a two-year-old."

I began more and more to see that there was something in this letting-up. I was frequently amazed at the speeding of the hours when one is just "setting," doing nothing, and the after feeling of complete relaxation followed by a resiliency of spirit. It gradually dawned upon me that the world wasn't, after all, made for us to work in all the time, and that to sit with a blank mind (and a dropped jaw) had in it a grain of something that I had not found in a continuous stream of effort. I announced this important discovery to The Lady one day when she seemed particularly receptive to having a great truth burst upon her. I classified it as "remarkable."

"It is," she agreed. "It must be, since it has taken you a life-time to find it out."

There *is* no pleasing a wife!

III

An early discovery of my leisure was the wide interest to be found in the daily newspaper. I had always read the paper from the point of view of my business. I read the building news carefully: the rest of the paper I merely glanced at. Now, from habit, I find myself merely glancing at the building news and carefully reading the rest of the paper.

I found I needed just that: to have my horizon expanded. A man immersed in cement as I have been for thirty years, with a corporation on his back growing to large proportions and increasing responsibilities, finds himself almost entirely with friends of his own and allied interests. I have known pleasantly the leading men in my own line, architects, engineers, contractors, constructors, and the like,—interesting men. You cannot deal with plans for great tunnels, bridges, dams or sky-scrapers without catching the romance of it or the thrill of achievement. But, after all, my interests with them began and ended in cement.

My evenings were chiefly spent at home, too tired to go out. I had to rest up for the next day's strain. Or I was in hotels in other cities on business of the company, closing contracts, attending conferences or conventions, with most of the after-dinner hours up to bed-time concerned with business. It was a life devoted to business, and practically nothing else. We say of some wives that they are golf-widows. What I marvel at is the patience with which thousands of wives endure the rôle of business widows.

IV

Not for a moment would I belittle the value of the contacts which a man makes in his chosen line of work. There are things large and fine that lie at hand in every business, no matter how dull it may sound or seem. The thrill of achievement is present in every line.

I remember standing once with four men before a gigantic building just finished. The Vice-President of the corporation for which the huge structure was intended was one of the group.

"A wonderful monument to your President," I remarked.

"Yes," answered the Vice-President. "Except that he is too lively for a monument yet."

"Ever see this?" he asked as he handed out a photograph of a superb mausoleum which had just been finished for the family of the President of whom we were speaking.

"Why the river and the coal-barge on the plaque in the front door?" I asked.

"That is supposed to be his father at the helm, with his mother sitting on the cabin with our President as a baby in her arms," he replied with a simple pride.

"Where was he born?" I asked.

"In the cabin of that barge somewhere on the Hudson River. There was a storm, the empty barge rocked some and he came before medical help could be had."

From such an origin!

V

One of the Governors present—the executive of one of the largest States in the Union—spoke up: "Talking about that sort of thing, I made an address at a meeting held in a hotel the other day where only eleven years ago I was a waiter working my way up. It was a curious feeling."

"You have nothing on me," broke in the other Governor—this time the Governor of a Western State: "My father was a mason who worked for his $1.50 per day and laid a goodly portion of the bricks in the Governor's Mansion in which I now live."

"You men all know —— ——, the President of our corporation," said the other "captain of industry" present. "I was thinking along exactly this line the other day when I was presiding at one of the Board meetings in his absence. We increased his salary to $250,000 a year. He came to us as a boy at 50 cents a day sorting the white rags from the colored pieces."

"And the secret?" I asked as I looked around at the men.

"No secret. Just work," said the Vice-President.

"Right," commented the Governors.

The point that some young men of to-day overlook.

VI

One of the few figures in our national life I came to know was Herbert Hoover, with whom, as Secretary of Commerce, my business threw me into contact. On one occasion I was told this story by one of his chief assistants.

It seems that two boys were working their way through Leland Stanford University. Their funds got desperately low, and the idea came to one of them to engage Paderewski for a piano recital and devote the profits to their board and tuition. The great pianist's manager asked for a guarantee of $2,000. The boys went ahead and staged the concert. They worked hard, only to find that the concert had totalled them only $1,600. So, after the concert, the boys sought the pianist, told him of their effort and result, and handed him the entire $1,600, accompanying it with a promissory note for $400 and explaining that they would earn the amount at the earliest possible moment and send the money to him.

"No, boys," returned Paderewski, "that won't do." Then, tearing up the note and returning the $1,600 to the boys, he said to them: "Now, take out of this your expenses, give yourselves each ten per cent of the balance for your work, and let me have the rest."

The years rolled by, the Great War came and went, and Paderewski was striving with might and main to

feed the starving thousands of his beloved Poland.
There was only one man in the world who could help
Paderewski and his people. Before he could stretch
forth his hand for help, thousands of tons of food began to come into Poland for distribution by the Polish
Premier. After the starving were fed, Paderewski
journeyed to Paris to thank Herbert Hoover for the
relief sent him.

"That's all right, Mr. Paderewski," was Hoover's
reply. "I knew the need was great. Besides, you
don't remember it, but you helped me once when I
was a student at college, and I was in a hole."

VII

I told this one day to a cousin who was interested
in the business management of Paderewski, and he
told me this story of which he was a part. It seems
that de Pachmann, the erratic pianist, cherishes for
Paderewski a curious feeling of intense jealousy. One
evening de Pachmann was at a table in a hotel dining-
room with his fellow artists Bachaus and Rosenthal
when the latter saw the manager of Paderewski passing by. He hailed him and asked: "How came you
here?"

"I am with Paderewski," was the reply. "We have
been dining in his suite up-stairs."

De Pachmann had just deposited a spoonful of
soup in his mouth. When he heard the remark, he

jumped up, spat out the soup, gave the table-cloth a vigorous pull and landed dishes on his guests and the floor, and shrieked out: "Don't eat that food. Don't eat it."

The dining-room was in an uproar, the head-waiter ran to the table, while de Pachmann, wildly gesticulating, roared out, "If he is here, there's poison in my soup and he has paid for it," and nothing that could be said or done by his friends could quiet the excited artist.

VIII

Paderewski has a delicious and quiet sense of humor, told my cousin. He said that on one Atlantic voyage Paderewski and Josef Hofmann were joint passengers. The two pianists are very close friends. Hofmann, as is well known, is an expert mechanician and his specialty of late has been improvements on automobiles, for which he has taken out a number of patents. He is an excellent automobile driver. Paderewski knows this, so that when a fellow passenger asked Paderewski where he placed Hofmann among pianists, his reply was ready: "I think he is the greatest pianist I know among chauffeurs."

IX

On one occasion when my company was doing a large piece of work for the Atchison, Topeka and

Santa Fé Railroad I visited its President, Mr. Ripley, at his home at Santa Barbara, California. After our business conference, he suggested golf, and he introduced me to my partner, who turned out to be Robert T. Lincoln, then with the Pullman Company. I confess that I played badly, being quite taken with the thought that I had as a partner the son of Abraham Lincoln, and I was more concerned with talking to him than with any anxiety about our side winning.

This acquaintance was recalled to me not long since when I heard a coincidental story that struck me as unbelievable until I wrote Mr. Lincoln, recalling our fatal golf game, and asking if the story could be true. It was only when Mrs. Lincoln, writing for her husband, answered saying that Mr. Lincoln asked her to say to me that it was true, that I believed it.

It seems that Robert Lincoln was twenty-two years old when his father, Abraham Lincoln, was shot. Young Lincoln was, in 1865, in the army stationed in Virginia when he received an order to report to Washington. He arrived late in the evening, went to the White House, where he was told that his father and mother had gone to Ford's Theatre. He went over to the theatre, and arrived there just in time to find the audience in an uproar and his father being carried out. He immediately went to his father's side.

In the administration of President Garfield, Mr. Lincoln was Secretary of War. He intended to accompany the President to Elberon, New Jersey. Finding that an important last-moment matter would prevent, Mr. Lincoln hurried to the station to explain the situation to the President, only to arrive there to hear a shot, see President Garfield fall, and go to his side.

When President McKinley went to Buffalo to attend the Exposition, Mr. Lincoln was also invited and reached the city at the moment when the President was shot by Czolgosz, and again hurried to the President's side.

When President Harding asked Mr. Lincoln to attend the formal opening of the Lincoln Memorial at Washington, some three years ago, the latter remarked to a friend, as he himself told these facts: "If they only knew, they wouldn't want me there. There seems to be a fatality about Presidential affairs when I am present." But, upon that occasion, the rule did not hold.

X

Speaking of Washington, you and I might stand and look at the fountain in the foreground of the United States Treasury Building at Washington—as perhaps we have—and it would mean to us nothing more than a fountain. "What else can it mean to any one?" some one will ask. Well, it is curious how an inanimate object such as a fountain may take a posi-

tive place and become a mark in our lives. Take the
case of a boy who, now some years ago, saw that fountain for the first time on April first. He was to begin
that day as a messenger boy in the Treasury Department, and one of his duties was to bring up buckets
of coal from the cellar underneath that fountain.
Now buckets of coal for a little undersized lad are
very heavy, and when the boy would reach the first
landing on the stairs he would put his buckets down,
rest at the window for a moment and look out at the
fountain. He did this every day, and the fountain
came to mean a resting-place for his tired little arms.
Then, for the rest of the day, he would sit on a chair,
waiting to be sent on errands, and again he would look
out of the window and see the fountain. One day a
man handed the boy a book, advised him to read it
in his leisure, study what was in it and it would be of
use to him in his later life. The book was a volume of
Blackstone's Commentaries. The boy read. Then
to school he went to find out what it all meant, and
in four years he graduated and passed the Bar as a
lawyer. But in walking along the lane that led to
the Bar he must have strayed off into some by-path,
for one day he found himself once more in front of the
Treasury fountain, and passed it to take a clerkship
in the Treasury Building. Again he saw the fountain,
—this time from another window, for now he sat at a
desk. Then after a bit he went to another desk to be

of help to the Assistant Secretary of the Treasury, and when that officer resigned, he graduated to his desk. The vision of stepping up just one more rung on the ladder was now naturally in the mind of the Assistant Secretary. Until one day it was proposed to him whether he would not like to see the Treasury fountain from the other side of the street. The young clerk thought he would.

And on the morning of the first day of every April those who knew could see a man standing at the plate-glass window just at the right of the main entrance of the great and powerful bank across the street from the Treasury Building. Quietly would he stand and look out at the fountain in the foreground and the huge Government building beyond. His gaze would fix itself on a window before which, not so many years ago, he daily rested his buckets of coal and gave a respite to his spent little arms. It was only for a brief few moments that he would stand there. Little time he had for reverie, but his secretary never disturbed her chief in those moments on that day, for she knew how precious were the memories that were awakened in those moments in the mind of the President of the Riggs Bank.

XI

Some years ago my wife met Mrs. Richard Mansfield, the wife of the actor, a friendship sprung up between the two women, with the result that the husbands met.

I was to have luncheon with Mansfield one day. The day was a wicked one. I had seldom seen or been in such a downpour of rain. We were just to begin luncheon in the actor's hotel sitting-room when word came that a messenger was down-stairs with a "rush" telegram. When the boy came, Mansfield took the despatch, and then his eye fell on the boy's badly-worn pair of shoes, which were soaked through.

"See here," said the actor, "your feet are soaking wet, aren't they?"

"Yes, sir," answered the boy in a frightened voice. His eyes were bulging out in looking at the famous actor, and to be really spoken to by this great man was too much for the boy.

"Well, that won't do at all," said Mansfield, now thoroughly aroused to the boy's feet. Laying the telegram aside unopened, and looking about the room, he said: "Now, see here, you just take off that rubber coat of yours, and we'll hang it over this chair, see?" Which was done. "Now, you here," he continued as he drew a chair before the open fire. "Sit right here," and to the astonishment of the boy—and to my own, I confess—the carefully valeted actor got down on his knees before the boy. "Now give me a foot." The boy, now perfectly dazed, dumbly obeyed, and in a moment the actor had the shoe unlaced and dropped

it on the floor. "Heavens, boy, your foot is soaked."
Then into the bathroom the actor fairly ran for two
towels. Then, turning to me, he asked: "Will you
please ring for my valet? Now, we'll have that stock-
ing off in a jiffy." Then Mansfield took the boy's foot
and dried and rubbed it with the towel. "Now,
that foot on this stool, see? Give me the other foot."

XII

Then to the amazed valet, as immaculate as his
employer, Mansfield turned: "See here, this boy's
feet are soaked. His shoes are full of holes. Take you
this shoe to the nearest shoe-store, match it for size,
and fetch me a pair of good strong shoes. Better make
it two pair," he added, and then ended with: "Shake a
leg now, won't you?"

The operation went on with the other foot. Then
a puzzled expression came on the face of the actor.

"Stockings, of course. I should have sent for stockings. Well, never mind. Mine will be large for you,
boy, but they'll do until you get home." And into
the next room the actor fairly dove, bringing back two
pair of silk hose! "Well," commented the beaming
actor, "they're big for you, son, but you can get
home in them, and then your mother can give them
to your father."

The boy, too dazed, had not spoken a word. I

don't think he could have uttered a word. His eyes followed every move of the actor.

Then came the shoes. "Now, let's see," he said as one shoe slipped on. "Now, stand on that one," and the boy did. "By Jove, see that," turning to me, "perfect fit. Now for the other," and that was slipped on. "Now, let's see. Stand up. Fine, by Jove, fine. Your feet won't get wet in those, son." Then seeing the other pair in a box, he smiled. "Well, you can't wear two pair of shoes at once, can you?"

"No, sir," came from the delighted boy.

"Tell you what," he said to the valet, "wrap this box up in that paper, see?" and turning to the boy, "then when that pair is worn out, you can start on this pair."

"Now, you're fixed up all right." Then: "Where's your slip, and I'll sign it. Now," turning to his valet, "his coat," and the boy's coat was slipped on him by the valet.

"Here's your slip," he said to the boy, "and a dollar for you. Not for your company, but for you, just for you, see?"

"Yes, sir," and the boy edged toward the door. He was too overcome to say thank you, but as he reached the door he turned his face on Mansfield, and such a loving glance as came from that boy must have repaid the actor more than the spoken word which would not come!

XIII

A different Mansfield than the public was accustomed to know from the stories current about him.

But it was the real Richard Mansfield, a gentleman of the stage!

CHAPTER FOUR

WHICH OF THE TWO?

At dinner the other evening I witnessed and thought much of one of those tragic instances so frequently met in our American life where the husband seemingly outstrips the wife.

CHAPTER FOUR

WHICH OF THE TWO?

I

THE man in this case was one of the foremost rail-road officials in the country. He had risen to his great position from his start as a section-hand. At that time he had married: not above or below his station, but a girl in his own walk in life. His unquestioned ability as an executive soon manifested itself, and he stepped naturally and easily from position to position. As he rose higher it meant, of course, that he associated with men superior in education. He was not slow to learn from them. His world grew larger: his outlook widened, and his mind expanded with his opportunities. The railroad business is naturally one of diversified interests and can, of itself, be a liberal education to a man, no matter how humble his beginning or what his lack of opportunity in early life. He read along economic lines until he became, as he is to-day, an authority in his line, and one of the best-informed men in foreign relations. Naturally, a man of such calibre is sought after; his invitations were many and in numerous instances his wife was asked.

39

II

But how about the wife? Six children were the happy lot of this couple, and for twenty of her best years, while her husband was mentally expanding, she was at home in the nursery and concerned with the thousand and one problems of her children. Except in her high estate as a mother, she stood still. When her children were grown and left the home-nest, she was so well along in years that a widening knowledge could not come easy to her. It would have come with the same difficulty to the husband at a corresponding age if his mental advancement had begun at that time. The result is that the husband has acquired all the ease and polish of contact with the world, and carries his high position with credit. But the wife has remained practically the wife of the section-hand. And she shows it. Worse still, she realizes the cruel fact that she cannot take her place at her husband's side. She is not the mental equal of the women she meets at the social affairs where her husband takes her, and, with a cruelty that women unfortunately have in such instances, she is made to feel her lack of opportunity. Fortunately, in this case, the husband has retained his affection for the girl of his youth, and if he is aware that his wife is lacking in her capacities to grace her present position, he gives no sign of it. Entertaining on the scale which is expected of her is not easy, and her affairs are glaringly ear-marked with her short-comings. Her contact with the servants in her establishment, particularly with the male part, leaves much to be desired in management and finesse, and her management of her guests and her table show her incapacity. The furnishings of her home distinctly show the hand of the hired decorator, and none is more uncomfortable among them than the mistress. Yet, to live on a certain scale is imperative with her husband's position.

III

It is the opposite of another instance of the prosperous business man who found himself in a similar position, and could not understand why his wife did not grow as he had grown. Man-like he failed to see why his wife could not run a large house as he ran a large business. "I have my manager to whom I detail everything," he argued. "Why don't you get a housekeeper and detail everything to her?"—overlooking the fact that if his wife were to take him at his word he would be the first to notice the lack of a wife's touch in his home. The wife knew this, but the husband could not comprehend it, and so it happened, as happens in so many similar cases, that the husband tired of the choice of his early days, got a divorce, married a woman more in touch with his present position, only to find that she soon began to find the same lacks in him which he found in his first wife. That he hadn't calculated upon.

It was this man who said to his first wife: "The trouble is that when we married we were both sparrows, but I have grown to be an eagle while you have remained a sparrow."

Clever and cruel,—desperately cruel. Yet true! The husband naturally takes great flights into the world of affairs, but the wife remains at home and chirps to the children. What else can she do? Take the flight of the eagle with him, and refuse to have children and be a sparrow?

IV

We have much to say in praise of the marvellous growth of our great men from lowly jobs to positions of commanding power and wealth, and no one certainly would hinder them in their development. But do we not fool ourselves when we assume that their rise in the world is all skittles and beer? All too often —some apparent and some not—there is the tragedy of a wife who has not kept pace.

V

The action of the husband in the latter instance was that of the coward, and, as in all actions of this kind, his chickens are coming home to roost.

But the husband and the wife of the first story? What about them?

The husband: a distinct force in the economic life of America, large of achievement.

The wife: the mother of six, the elder three boys of which have already stepped into affairs and are, in so far as the record of a few brief years can show, making good as men.

Both are serving their generation, each in his and her way: he receiving the benefit of the expansion of his work: she, apparently, retarded, from a social view-point, by reason of her work.

Who, in the largest sense, is fulfilling?

Which of the two?

CHAPTER FIVE
TWO WOMEN

We have had great sport, my wife and I, in selecting the woman we like best of these two, and then presenting the reasons for the choice. Perhaps you will enjoy the same mental fun.

CHAPTER FIVE
TWO WOMEN

THE FIRST:

I

WE had been invited and prevailed upon to accept an invitation to a club meeting in a near-by community where "the most distinguished authoress of the day" was to read from her own books and tell some of her experiences.

It sounded fine. But The Lady had happened to have met "the most distinguished authoress of the day," and from what she told me of her and as I knew the club she was scheduled to address, I couldn't mentally see two and two making four there. I was curious to see how it would come out, and we went.

The assembly-room was packed. Every member who could crowd in was present to hear "the most distinguished authoress of the day." It was an audience of a quality that any speaker might well be proud to address—provided the speaker had a message! But had "the most distinguished authoress of the day" a message? I couldn't see that she had. Her name, yes, was on every one's lips from her "best sellers." But not all "best sellers" are necessarily "best books." Then, the lady herself! Spoke truly the man who said that authors should be read, but never seen or heard.

II

The President, in a few well-phrased prefatory sentences, explained that "the most distinguished authoress of the day" was forced to catch a train directly after the reading and that therefore the reception which so many had asked should be held to give them the opportunity to meet "the m. d. a. o. t. d." would be held in the reception-room back of the stage during the fifteen-minute intermission. At which announcement there was a pleasant buzz of pleasant anticipation, and much clapping of hands until——

"The most distinguished authoress of the day" appeared that moment on the platform. The applause stopped instantly! The men chuckled and nudged each other and put their hands over their mouths. The women gasped, and scores raised their lorgnettes only to put them down very quickly. It wasn't really possible for a woman to have worn less and be dressed, and when she turned around to lay her vanity-box on the table, the V of the back was flush with the waist!

First round! No decision.

"Before I read from my favorite book, which I understand is also yours," said Madame Distin-

guished Authoress, "I will tell you a few anec-
dotes."

Whereupon she did, and the men wished she hadn't
—whatever the women thought. The girls giggled:
they were not only scenting forbidden fruit: they
were tasting it and were pulsating with thrills!

Second round! A decision all right, but "the most
distinguished authoress" was not aware of it, although
the lack of applause and laughter might have told any
one a trifle more subtle or telepathic!

III

Then she read from her "favorite book" and theirs!
But she might just as well have stopped!

"And now," said The Most Distinguished Authoress, "as you have been told so graciously by your
President, I shall be glad to meet any of you in the
room back of the stage, where I am going to enjoy a
cigarette."

Fatal ending! It was the finishing touch! The
smokers in that audience were men!

A deadly silence reigned over that packed hall, except the girls, who chuckled with glee and whispered
in each other's ears and drowned their giggles in their
handkerchiefs. No one moved. It was evident that
The Most Distinguished Authoress of the Day was
not to meet a single one of "you," and yet they were

too well-bred to walk out before the close. Finally
the President, sensing that something must be done,
arose and started for "back stage," urging this one
and that one to come with her as she went her soli-
tary way. But a universal shake of heads was all that
she got. It was like the famous occasion when:

> "Smarty Marty had a party
> Nobody came but a blue-eyed darkey."

"Not a world-series line of your people to meet
me," observed The Most Distinguished Authoress of
the Day, as the President entered the "star's" dressing-
room. "I don't seem to have made an exciting hit
with your people. I'll snap them up some more when
I go out. It's good for them. They're stodgy."

She did. But the next day, the local bookstore,
which had laid in a generous stock of the books of
The Most Distinguished Authoress of the Day on
commission, and had filled its window with them, returned the entire shipment to the publishers. "No
demand," was his laconic comment. It was all expressed, as they say in cross-word puzzles, in one
word of five letters beginning with F and ending with
T!

The Most Distinguished Authoress of the Day
had gotten away from her kind. She had stood herself on her head, and her poor little marbles had all
tumbled out of her pocket!

IV

I heard a good story at this melancholy "reading," however. It was told of a clever Boston physician who was present. This doctor is likewise a clever student of human nature. He is very popular at social occasions, and at such times his lady-patients are not above the attempt of obtaining gratuitious medical advice from him. The clever Mrs. Saunders, or at least she regarded herself as clever, was one of these, and when the doctor cheerfully greeted the lady at a musicale with an inquiry as to how she was, she answered: "Quite well, Doctor, only, as you see from my red nose, I have a dreadful cold."

"So sorry," answered the physician, on the alert for the next move.

"Now, Doctor, I know you are not supposed to practise when you are out socially, but would you just tell me, in a word, what is the best thing for a cold such as mine?"

"Surely, Mrs. Saunders," cheerfully answered the physician, as he started to move away. "I should recommend a handkerchief, madam, and if you find one is not enough, I would try two."

Which is on a par with that excellent answer made by Judge Gary, of the Steel Trust, to a woman who took him aside at a dinner party, and said, almost in a whisper: "Judge, would you mind telling me if you

think steel stock is going up or down?" "Certainly,"
replied the urbane Judge, "I think it will. You see,
madam, it rarely ever stands still, and it cannot very
well go sideways."

Which reminds me of the ruse attempted on an
equally clever London specialist whose fee was four
guineas for a patient's first visit to his office and two
guineas for any subsequent visit. A patient, recommended to this physician, figured out how he could
avoid the four-guinea fee and get on the basis of the
two-guinea fee from the start. Knowing that the
specialist had a large practice, and figuring that he
was not likely to remember all his patients, he entered
the doctor's office with the cheerful salutation: "Well,
doctor, here I am *again*," with a special emphasis on
the last word.

"Yes," answered the doctor, scenting the situation,
"what can I do for you this time?"

"The same thing," answered the patient, jubilant
at the two guineas saved. "Same old throat, you
know. Pretty bad this time."

"Is it?" queried the doctor. "Well, then, I would
go right on and use the same prescription I gave you
when you were here before."

TWO WOMEN

The Second

I

The doctors had, for fourteen years, laid in her arms some four-score little babies that had been sent to this old world to freshen it: to enrich women's love and to make men better. And she had, in the matter-of-fact manner of nurses, taken the precious charges handed her, wrapped them up in warm, soft blankets, laid them on convenient couches—and, seemingly, forgotten them!

She had seen the most wonderful and awe-inspiring happening in the world occur so often—and so variously.

Eight times in one year: that was the record. Two, in that year, had liked it better in Heaven's playground, and had quickly slipped back. It was so much more beautiful there. Warmer, too. Gentler.

She had seen mothers, too, remain in The Valley of Rest.

She had witnessed pain—pain to wring the stout hearts of doctors who had quailed before it. But she had stood firm—ready at her post. Of course, she belonged to The Weaker Sex. But she could not show it.

She had seen, so often, that moment in a woman's life when the gates of Heaven swing ajar just for an instant, and when a vision is given her, and her alone.

She had seen that glory that is of God as it comes into a woman's eyes as her first-born is laid in her arms for the first time.

She had seen, too, that supreme moment when the child draws its life for the first time from its mother's breast—that moment when, after the first draught, a look of serenity transfuses the face, and the woman becomes the Madonna.

She had seen the first smiles of mothers.

But she had, too, closed the eyes of mothers.

She had seen the Curtain of Life lift: she had seen the Curtain of Life fall.

It was much for one woman to see.

II

And yet——

"I hope before very long to have a little life of my own like that in my arms," she said very simply one morning as she was bathing the little mite. Her face was suffused with color as the little one nestling in her arms opened its eyes, looked into the kindly face bending over it, and cooed its approval to her.

The man, standing by, was filled with silent wonder. He had just witnessed the little woman of his heart go through the valley and barely emerge.

"You?" he heard himself ask.

The nurse quickly looked up into the face of masculine incredulity. "Yes, indeed," was the hearty reply. "Why not?"

The man was silent.

"Y-e-s," he finally stammered. "Of course. Why not?" he echoed. And with a desperate attempt to get out of the situation somewhere he ended exactly where he began: "Y-e-s. Of course. Why not?"

The woman smiled. She knew what was in the groping mind.

"You see," came the calm words of the nurse, "I have seen this wonderful thing happen so often to other women. I want that moment of all the ages to come to me. It belongs to a woman. You men don't understand."

The man thought—for several moments: quietly.

Then he muttered once more "Y-e-s" feebly.

III

That night he fell asleep in wonderment of it all. Particularly of Man as The Stronger Sex.

CHAPTER SIX
THE REAL MRS. GRUNDY

I wonder if you will believe it when you have finished this. For it *is* hard to believe!

CHAPTER SIX

THE REAL MRS. GRUNDY

I

I DON'T know how it is with others, but I had always regarded Mrs. Grundy as a mythical character. I had bracketed her with Mrs. Partington, Billy Patterson, and all the other figments of the brains of clever folk. Hence I was filled with amazement when, visiting at my sister's house in the South, she said: "I am so glad you have come, for I have been wanting to give you the surprise of your life. I am going to take you next door and introduce you to one of the most famous women of the world. I don't suppose there are a hundred people who know she is alive, and I don't suppose there are that number who ever believed there was such a woman."

"Who is she?" I asked.

"Mrs. Grundy," came the answer.

"What Mrs. Grundy?" I inquired, forgetting grammar in my excitement.

"*The* Mrs. Grundy. 'What will Mrs. Grundy say?' and all that!" came the laughing answer.

"But—" I began, and I immediately thought of Thomas Morton's play, the character of Mrs. Grundy who was a sort of "Mrs. Harris" to Dame Ashfield, and so on.

"I know," replied my friend. "It seems incredible, doesn't it? Born in England, she left England as a young girl, came to New England, married Giles Grundy,—who excused himself and took to an early grave, glad to get there I fancy,—and now is his widow, living here where she came fifteen years ago because of the climate, quietly, with not even the neighbors knowing who she is. But she wants to meet you, else you never would have known."

"But how old is she, a hundred or a thousand?" I asked, in wonderment.

"In her ninety-fourth year, but as chipper as a robin. See?" as she pointed to a window next door, where was sitting a white-haired woman as tranquil as you please. "Always at the window. As much interested in the town's doings as usual: full of gossip about the people she doesn't know or who do not know her, watchful of every movement of the neighbors, weaving all sorts of rumor and scandal about them. The same Mrs. Grundy as she always was. Come, let's go over. She's waiting for you."

II

Within five minutes I was shaking hands with and looking into the smiling face of certainly the best-known woman of two continents.

"Well, I am very glad to see you," was her greeting. "I have heard so much about you from your sister. Saw you and your wife arrive yesterday. Very sweet face, hasn't she? And you have time to come and see a garrulous old lady, have you? Very nice of you. I am ninety-four, you know, almost ninety-five. But I don't feel old at all. Lovely here—this climate, and so many people going and coming on the street. Quite like old times. Yes, I know 'em all, although they don't know me. Don't want 'em to know. Dear me," she laughed a rich, full laugh, "wouldn't they be surprised? They speak my name, I dare say, hundreds of times. I suppose you have heard dreadful things about me, haven't you?" she finally ended up with.

"Hardly dreadful," I managed to get in.

"I know you are polite. But, tell me the truth, were you not surprised to hear I was alive: that I ever was alive? Curious, isn't it, how people think of me as some one who never existed. Odd, because I talked enough and did what people called damage. But, my son, it wasn't so damaging as folks made it out to be. I gave women something to do: to think about: to talk about. In my day, the days were not as full as they are now. Life was not so crowded. Women led terribly constricted lives: Puritanic in New England. I made up my mind to stir them up, and I did, didn't I?" with again the hearty laugh.

"I certainly got people by the ears. Poor Giles. I am afraid I led him an uncomfortable life. He was kept busy morning, noon, and evenings denying that I had said this and intimated that. Life grew too busy for him: the threads got too complicated, and off he went. I don't blame him for going. Poor soul."

III

The stream of talk steadily went on.

It reminded me of the German orchestral conductor who, whenever he corrected his oboe player, brought down upon himself a perfect torrent of explanation. Finally, at a rehearsal, he could endure it no longer, and broke out with: "Here, you, when I correct you, don't shpoke so much. Den und now, yes, but always, my God, never!"

"I had a lovely time having read to me not long ago," continued Mrs. Grundy without a break, "a chapter called 'Memorials of Mrs. Grundy' in a book called, Charlotte what is the name of that book you read to me? Oh, yes, *My Unknown Chum*. Read it? Well, the author has a chapter about me in it. He must have been a New England man, and evidently he knew me, because he refers so feelingly (with a chuckle) to Giles. He has a lot to say of my tireless tongue, lovely! but the cleverest thing he says is that when I established the first sewing circle, there was more talking than sewing, and that the sewing circle became to the Protestant Church what the confessional is to the Roman Church. Isn't that delicious? And he was not far from right, either," she added as she nodded her head. "He frankly says I am not a myth, but a widow and adds 'a terrible reality.' Isn't that an awful thing to say of one? He says that in our sewing circle reputations were treated just as garments: cut out and fitted and basted and sewed up. Clever, isn't it? He says I did more harm than all the other women in the Parsfield parish put together, which, of course, is all nonsense. No single woman *can* do the harm that a group of women can do (Lovely angle!) These women were eating their hearts out with loneliness, and I just brought them together and made them companionable. Of course, we had to talk about something, and what more interesting subject in a small town than your neighbors? We had lovely times, and I often look back upon them with envy. As for doing harm, that is nonsense. We would occasionally get some of our neighbors by the ears, but it was good for them. It is what the town needed. So did the church. Whenever we had a meeting of the circle, the members would come and wonder 'What will Mrs. Grundy say?' That's the way that remark started, and it became a by-word. But as for saying that I broke up homes and divided families—bosh! I lived in that town twenty-six years and never knew of a home broken up or a family divided except of their own doing. Of course, lots of unfortunate rows were laid at my door, but, tush! that is always a handy way of directing attention away from one's self." And then with her eyes atwinkle, and with a laugh that was really delicious, she looked at my sister and me and added, "I may have been naughty once in a while with my tongue: every woman is, but I was never really bad. Come from too good English stock for that!" she ended with a toss of the grey head.

IV

I looked at this remarkable woman. It was an interesting face, finely chiselled: her eyes sparkling with glee as she went on: "Looking me over, aren't you? Well, how do you find me? I *would* like your impression. Tell me. Do I look like the terrible gossip and trouble-maker you have heard so much about? You can tell me, but don't tell others. This little house couldn't hold the curiosity seekers and the townspeople would get afraid that I would, how do you say it now, yes, that's it, start something. I do, too, only the folks don't know it. I like to weave all kinds of stories, good and bad, about people. I sit here and do it all day. Charlotte, my niece, you know, reads the local paper to me, all the doings of people in the town who live here and who come here for the winter: points them out to me when they pass, and then I make up the most wonderful stories about them. Some of them are true, too, I find later. Telepathic? Yes, I think I am. But I do no one any harm, as your sister will tell you. I am too old, now. Oh, yes, my sight is splendid: I can see everything and everybody that passes, and I see lots of things that are not so," and once more that deep, hearty, infectious laugh!

One couldn't help liking the old lady. But I couldn't get over the idea that there existed an actual Mrs. Grundy, and there she sat!

"Mustn't tell people, though, that I am here. You are not a writing man, are you? Come to think of it, I wouldn't mind if you were, and wrote about me, so long as you gave no clue to where I lived. Wouldn't it be fun, Charlotte?" she asked of her niece. "Do you think any one could do it without revealing my whereabouts? I can see the eyes of women pop out, and hear them say: 'Why, I didn't know there really was a Mrs. Grundy, did you?' And here she is, not only real, but alive—very much so, eh! Charlotte? Do you know, the more I think of it, the more delicious it seems. Share your surprise with some writer, if you wish, but tell him to be very, very careful, son, won't you? You see I can call you son, old as you are. Why, I can remember three decades, think of it, before you were born."

"Just didn't believe there ever was such a woman, isn't that it?" she asked.

I acknowledged it.

"Yes, to millions I am a myth, until I pass away and join Giles. Then the newspapers will come out and astonish thousands. In my younger days I was always sorry I couldn't stand on the curb and see myself ride by. Now, I am sorry I won't be able to see the newspapers when I take my last ride, and read their astonished comment. Can't you imagine it?"

I assured her I readily could, just as I can imagine the amazement writ on the faces of all who read what I have written here of my astonishing discovery which, as far as I can, I share with my astonished readers.

A living Mrs. Grundy! It seems so incredible.

CHAPTER SEVEN
WHEN WE CROWN-PRINCED

"I have accepted an invitation at the Holmes's to-day for you and me to meet the Crown Prince and Princess of Sweden at luncheon," was The Lady's announcement one morning.

"Title-hunting?" I ventured.

"Not at all," was the reply. "They are very interesting people on their own account."

I had heard that he was, at any rate, quite a man.

So we Crowned-Princed.

CHAPTER SEVEN

WHEN WE CROWN–PRINCED

I

Now, a man on a diet is not a very comfortable guest except to those few intelligent hostesses who have the discretion not to comment on what her guests are eating or, as in my case, not eating. There are such hostesses, praise be, but they are rare!

This "feast" was one of so many that are all so painfully alike in their absolute disregard of anything even approaching a sane combination of food: where the hostess seems hell-bent to select as many dishes as the market allows which even those with the ostrich variety of digestion cannot assimilate.

II

There was the ever-present grape-fruit to start off with, and then on top of it a tomato-purée soup—a combination that challenges rather briskly the healthiest digestive processes. Then, added to the mess, came a lobster salad and chicken croquettes (fried), and, to crown all, the feast ended with that worst of all combinations so dear to the heart of hundreds of unthinking hostesses, tomato salad with French dressing, followed by ice-cream! It would be hard to beat if it weren't so often beaten

III

But I had so often been the victim of these unintellingtly planned feasts that it is no longer any punishment for me to let course after course pass until at the end of the meal I find I have had for my meal a roll or a slice of butterless bread. It seems to be an unwritten custom (why no hostess has ever been able to explain to me!) that butter must never be served with bread at a formal luncheon or dinner. I have often asked why then the bread, and never yet have I been given a reason. It is not that I mind a foodless meal so much, because, with an interesting neighbor, one can forget his hunger. But even that was denied me at this particular luncheon. My host held the attention of the Crown Princess on my left, so I was left with one of those giggling and extravagant-speeched nineteen-year-old types of the modern girl that are so trying to one's nerves. She had been put there to observe what the Crown Princess wore and how the Crown Prince, diagonally across, ate, she told me. Such a feast! Taking my courage in my hand I began and asked the conventional question of how she liked our community, which she was visiting. "Oh," was the immediate reply, "I think it is the most wonderful place in the world." (She had been there exactly twenty hours!)

"Did you meet the Crown Prince?" was my next venture.

"Yes, I met him just before luncheon. Don't you think he's simply p-e-rfect? He is really precious!" She had spoken to him just two minutes!

She had played tennis that morning, I learned, and I rested on that next, and asked how she had found the courts.

"Oh, they're perfectly adorable, don't you think?"

The playing was "marvellous"; she had had "the most wonderful tennis of her life"—at nineteen!

IV

"There is no place in the whole world like this," she assured me. I soon found that the "world" was the smallest unit in her vocabulary. Our host came next for an inquiry, and to him she applied her pet superlative of being "simply divine." When the ice-cream was served, that was also "divine." Iced tea also came within the divinity realm. And so it went on. She "adored" this; she was "simply mad" about that; she was "just intense" about one man who was "heavenly" and another who was "a precious dear." Within fifteen minutes there was scarcely a superlative in the language which she had not misused.

Opposite to me sat her father, a practical and successful man of affairs. I could see a twinkle in his eye as he looked over to me and heard the battery of adjectives coming from his empty-headed little daughter. I could almost hear him think: "Don't mind it. It's a period. It goes with nineteen. It will pass away." But will it? Does it? Where is the period in the beginning of the rightful use and relative value of words? I have heard these poor little empty heads still saying at thirty that they "are mad" about things, "crazy" over this, and something else is "divine." The value of seldom-used adjectives is gone, because it never existed. It's a "period," yes. But as to its passing away, that is, as this precious young person assured me, "something entirely else again!"

It was not what I called a memorable luncheon. There was, for me at least, nothing to eat—and nothing to talk to!

V

The men now adjourned to the library, and I made up my mind to get a line on the Crown Prince, who had favorably impressed himself on a number of men. But before I knew it His Royal Highness was at my side.

"Excuse me," he said in perfect English, "I understand that you have just retired from business, and I want to ask if you will be so good as to give me your view-point. As I have seen American business men they have not the habit, I should say, of retiring from business at your age and vigor," with a smile. "Am I wrong?" he added.

I gave the young Prince my angle on the situation. Then came question after question. Intelligent, too. He was certainly out for information. He was about as good a listener as I ever talked to. When he had apparently gotten all he wanted on the retirement question, he asked: "You mentioned, I think, your business was cement. That is coming very largely into vogue with us in Sweden as a building material. Will you tell me something about it: its ingredients and, particularly, its durability?"

Of course, I was on familiar ground, and so I held forth until the host interrupted us, when with a most gracious smile he said: "Will you excuse me just for a few moments? I am deep in cement." And back he came to the attack. I could see he was not to be put off with partial information. He had all the thoroughness of the European.

"Thank you," he said at the close. "You will pardon my asking so many questions. But I am here, you know, in America to seek information."

He certainly was in the way of getting it!

It occurred to me how curious it was that it required the visit of this intelligent young scion to the throne of Sweden to prove the dismal failure of a similar

American visit of the scion to the throne of Great Britain.

VI

As the Prince turned to leave, he asked me: "Does it happen, by any chance, that your evening is free?"

I told him it was.

"I wonder if you will pardon the short invitation? But will you dine with me at the —— Club at eight o'clock? I am asking just a handful of men. Nothing formal, I assure you. Your dinner coat will, I am sure, be comfortable."

VII

The next morning when I had rehearsed to The Lady what a rattling good evening—and part of morning—I had enjoyed, I asked how she had gotten along at the Crown Princess's little dinner.

"Stupidly," she answered.

"Stupidly?" I echoed.

"Exactly. In spite of the Crown Princess's injunction that the little dinner was, like yours, purely informal, nearly every woman put on her fullest décolleté regalia, and at once made a formal affair of it. The Crown Princess did her best to break the ice and make it informal. But the ice would not break. The women were petrified in the presence of royalty and couldn't open their mouths."

"And what *did* you do?" I persisted.

"What women in such a group always do, honey. Looked each other over to see what each woman had on, and, particularly, in this case, what the Crown Princess wore."

"And she wore?" I asked.

"The simplest dress of any woman present."

"Why is it that women in such a group cannot have as good a time as we men have in such a group?" I asked.

"Why?" she remarked in surprise. "I've just told you. Every woman is too absorbed in what she has on and what the other woman has on. They can't get away from themselves. A woman is always self-conscious when she has her best bib on—never herself."

II

CHAPTER EIGHT
TOM

We were coming home from a day in the country. On the hall-table lay a heap of mail.

"Don't read that now," came my orders. "Let it go until to-morrow."

On top of the pile lay a letter from England. There was something about it that looked inviting. Welcome letters look like that!

"Only this one," I compromised.

CHAPTER EIGHT
TOM

I

THE letter was from a favorite young married couple of ours. The whole content of the letter was —a turtle! Not exciting, one might say offhand. But wait—and read. It was more.

II

This young couple and their little girl are great gardeners, as almost every one is in England, and their latest acquisition was a turtle. Now, a turtle doesn't mean much to us in America because we have little if any turtle-lore. But in England a turtle is an institution. He holds a place in English life apart from the cat or dog. In fact, the temperament of the turtle is most peculiarly English. It has a reserve without coldness: a fidelity above that of most all other animals (or humans). A turtle will live in a garden, as do the English. Indeed, an English turtle perishes quickly if kept long away from flowers or grass. Most English, too, is the turtle in a delicate affection which thrives on subtleties of tacit understandings. A turtle will crawl over to its owner's feet, withdraw a few paces and sit there for over an hour

with eyes rigidly fixed on its master's face without
wavering.

A turtle is, of course, of the snake family, an off-
shoot before birds, and of very ancient lineage, one
of the few of the Mesozoic era who carried on. His
period of hibernation, doubtless, helped him through
the destructive ice age. One of the things noted about
his sleeping is his extreme coldness. A turtle gradually grows icy cold before being completely in sleep.

III

Now this turtle in particular—Tom he was called
by the little girl of my friends—has a distinct personality, as you shall see. The extent to which I could
train him, wrote Tom's mistress, was truly amazing.
After a few of the natural accidents, I punished him
only by a severe slap on the head and tail, trying to
make him associate the punishment with the blunders.
No dog responded quicker. Presently he could be
carried for hours in the motor, providing I carried
him, with perfect cleanliness. After stroking him
under the chin for some minutes, he would purr the
daintiest single note, about as high as C middle on a
harpsichord. In warm weather this was very distinct.
Considering his prehistoric link with birds, this was
acutely interesting. I had once seen a snake charm a
canary till it dropped from its perch, but although I

tried Tom on several birds, he took no notice of his cousins. Both cat and dog remained suspicious of him, and refused to remain anywhere near him, although of course Tom had no possible method of attack. During a very warm week he gave three distinct tiny notes, and made the gr-r-r in his throat continuous for about a half minute at a time.

IV

Another interesting point about Tom is his sense of "attraction." There has been a controversy in the paper as to birds making their flights from and return to the same home over long distance by an extraordinary sense of "attraction" which a noted English scientist is proving to be due to their keen scent. He attests that when certain trees—once an oak-tree and again an almond-tree—were cut out of a garden the birds flew back to those same species of trees, but in other gardens. The scent of the reptile by which he will reach his mate over extraordinary distance is known. Directly the first spell of warm weather came, Tom was continually setting out, at quite a speed for him, up the garden-path and across some fields, slipping through the blocked hedge with real dexterity, and once removing a stone as big as himself (his fore legs are very strong). He was then always found at an old tin hut which had been abandoned for some years. After considerable questioning, the old village grocer tells me that the gypsies who lived there about seventeen years ago had two tortoises. By some long coincidence, indeed by what and why who will say, Tom knows this.

V

The village midwife has had her tortoise twenty-two years, who all through her hard life has been her silent, steady companion, asleep as well as awake. Directly her tortoise gets "sulky," that is sleepy, she puts him in a pretty box all lined with her garden's best flowers, and just places him beside her bed. He sleeps six moons, and wakes after the new moon of the seventh. He always goes to sleep on the opening of a new moon. Purposely I did not take Tom up when he began to be "sulky." I noticed about October fifteenth, when, given his bath in the pond, he floated but would not swim. He began to be very cold, and ate very little. A thick film like glue fastened his eyes and mouth and parts. A tortoise seems to lay up a special supply of food to store him over the winter, and he continually passes minute secretions in his sleep. Tom refused his two favorite foods: dandelion and columbine, and never touched those which lay by him all night. He chose a sheltered spot by the hedge, and began to bury himself. He

did not dig the earth out with his paws, but kept
wedging his body, sidling it, until a fairly good hole
was made. When I took him off he began again, very,
very slowly. Then he became icy cold. When I took
him out he was unrecognizable. His head was drawn
to the very inner centre, and also his tail, and sealed
with a thick mucous, and not visible in any way.
Only his claws could I see. This is the tortoise's de-
fense. His shell, however, seemed much thicker than
usual, darker and more oily. Nothing whatever
awakened him. Tom was as dead as an Indian fakir
can actually be in his three days' trance before resur-
rection. I was counselled to stick a pin in Tom, but
couldn't find it in my heart to do it, although I am
told it is often done without waking or hurting the
turtle. One tortoise in the village had its leg gnawed
off by rats, and did not even then awaken until its
lunar period. Thinking that the sun's heat might be
the cause of Tom's warmed blood's rebirth, I turned
on a high-powered electric bulb and left it hanging
over his box all day. The box and earth turned hot.
But Tom stirred not!

Last winter, in a burning house, a tortoise was
saved by a boy who remembered he was asleep inside
and heroically rescued him. The cardboard box holding the tortoise was completely burned, and yet the
animal, still in its undisturbed trance, did not awake
until at its own good time in April.

VI

But what is the relation of a dim English moon and a tortoise? It makes one almost believe that when the moon swung off from the whirling earth there may have been some fluid, some gas, some atom which found a kindred expression there as the cooling earth here expressed in its thousand years into Tom. Is there still some dim haunting cry, too fine, too shrill for the blunted human ear; but which this age-old creature catches in its easy subconsciousness? Or is it that He in whose consciousness the rhythms of moon and Tom are interchangeable, still binds them as one for his own unity, encompassing both?

VII

There, at any rate, is Tom. Not R. I. P., but only quiescent, abandoning consciousness, resuming consciousness, carrying on the traditions of a million years of nature's resurrections!

Christ would have understood. He could have unlocked Tom's doors of sleep. He could have rolled the stone away. But we can only wait for that which is the Christ in nature to awaken Tom when his days shall be accomplished.

For how true it is of this turtle that "lo! he is not dead, but sleepeth."

CHAPTER NINE

A WORLD OF LIMERICKS

I am told that there are various forms of some of these specimens of tabloid verse. I disclaim any knowledge as to which of these forms are correct and which are not. Nor do I accept any responsibility for the forms given in the following pages. I merely give them as amusing bits contributed to the limerick evening I tell about on the facing page. Hence, as no permanent form was intended, the question of absolute accuracy was not borne in mind. Nor is this in mind in the present publication. I say this because I do not want to get into correspondence or discussion with the hordes of limerick experts which I have learned exist all over this country. These clever specimens are given here merely as a reflection of an amusing evening.

CHAPTER NINE
A WORLD OF LIMERICKS

I

ONE evening, shortly after my retirement, I was at one of those dinner parties at the house of a friend which, when I was in business, I had been too tired to attend. A group of unusually bright people were there. One man was secretary of an organization I never knew existed: the London Limerick League. It was natural, therefore, that after dinner the talk turned on limericks, and "the Honorable Secretary," as he is termed, told about the method pursued in gathering limericks from every part of the world. When the talk ended, the company decided to form itself into a Limerick League, spend three months in gathering limericks, and then give a "limerick evening" at which each member would contribute a limerick. The public was to be charged an admission fee, the proceeds to go for the benefit of the parish house for which we were all trying to secure funds.

II

My previous business and social lines had been far afield from limericks. Hence I was surprised, as I take it some of my readers will be, to know the ex-

tent of the limerick field: that there are organizations
devoted to their collection in all parts of the world:
books devoted to them: a hobby, in other words,
ridden with a wide-spread diligence and assiduity of
which I was entirely ignorant. There is a world of
limericks apparently. The results of our collection
were highly amusing, and the "limerick evening" so
successful that it had to be repeated, not once but
twice, with the parish house fund coming in strong.

III

A limerick, if well done, has a quality of amuse-
ment all its own, and those collected for our "limerick
evening" were admirably selected. Of course, many
were old: some were new—to me at least. And because it is unlikely that all can be familiar to any
single person, I venture to share the best with the
readers of this book as promoters of a jolly evening.
I hope the authors of these limericks will not accuse
me of purloining their brain-children without credit,
since these specimens were collected over a wide area,
and their authorship was not obtained.

IV

Of course, the world-renowned of all limericks is
this one par excellence:

> Puella Rigensis ridebat,
> Quam tigris in tergo vehebat,

Externa profecto
Interno revecta
Sed risus cum tigre manebat!

Many believe the following to be the cleverest bit
of tabloid verse ever written, although, technically,
it is not a limerick:

> Little Willy, in the best of sashes,
> Fell in the fire and was burned to ashes.
> By-and-by the room grew chilly
> But no one liked to brush up Willy.

The limerick which won the next greatest degree of
pleasure on our limerick evening was this:

> There was a young lady named Lent
> Whose nose was most awfully bent.
> One day, I suppose,
> She followed her nose,
> But no one could tell where she went.

With this as a good third:

> There was a young warrior of Larmer,
> Who lovingly fondled his charmer,
> Said the maiden demure,
> "You'll excuse me, I'm sure,
> If I ask you to take off your armor."

This was very popular:

> There was a young fellow of Perth,
> Who was born on the day of his birth.

He was married, they say,
On his wife's wedding-day
And he died when he quitted the earth.

A clever runner-up was this one:

A thrifty young fellow named Shoreham
Made brown paper trousers and wore 'em.
He looked nice and neat
Till he bent in the street
To pick up a pin. Then—well he tore 'em!

V

Personally, I liked this as well as any:

Said a great Congregational preacher,
To a hen: "You're a wonderful creature."
And the hen, just for that,
Laid an egg in his hat,
And thus did the hen reward Beecher.

This one is not quite so familiar, yet its workman-
ship is good:

There was a faith-healer of Deal
Who said: "Although pain isn't real,
If I sit on a pin
And it punctures my skin,
I dislike what I fancy I feel."

Dean Inge, of Saint Paul's Cathedral, in London,
is quite a limerickist, I understand, and has perpe-
trated several, among which this is one of the best:

A certain young gourmet of Crediton
Took some pâté de foie gras and spread it on
A chocolate biscuit,
Then murmured "I'll risk it."
His tomb bears the date that he said it on.

To Dean Inge this one is also attributed:

Your verses, dear Friend, I surmise,
Were not meant for clerical eyes,
The Bishop and Dean
Cannot think what they mean
And the curate turns pink with surprise.

Thus did Dean Inge lay himself open to the following by one of his parishioners:

Our vicar is good Mr. Inge.
One evening he wanted to sing,
So we asked him to stoop,
Put his head in a loop,
Then we pulled at each end of the string.

Another playful one about a vicar is this:

An indolent vicar of Bray
His roses allowed to decay;
His wife, more alert,
Bought a powerful squirt
And said to her spouse, "Let us spray."

VI

A limerick full of feeling is this from a suburbanite:

There was a young man Thomas Pine
Put his head on the Long Island line;

But he died of ennui
For the 4:53
Didn't come till a quarter past nine.

Evidently Long Island offers abundant ammunition for limericks:

There was a young man from South Bay
Who was making some fireworks one day
But he dropped his cigar
In the gunpowder jar
There *was* a young man from South Bay.

This is reflective of far-away Japan:

There was a great swell in Japan
Whose name on a Tuesday began,
And lasted through Sunday
'Til twilight on Monday,
And sounded like stones in a can.

VII

This comes from England, and is considered among the best of English limericks:

Said a foolish young lady of Wales,
"A smell of escaped gas prevails."
Then she searched, with a light,
And later that night
Was collected—in several pails.

Daniel Gabriel Rossetti was such a confirmed addict to writing limericks that he wrote this one of himself:

There is a poor sneak called Rossetti,
As a painter with many kicks met he
With more than a man.
Thus ofttimes he ran,
And that saved the rear of Rossetti.

Very familiar, but always worthy of a new smile
is this one:

There once was an old man of Lyme,
Who married three wives at a time.
When asked, "Why the third?"
He replied, "One's absurd;
And bigamy, sir, is a crime!"

This is so remindful of the modern American business man:

There was an old bear at the Zoo
Who was feeling exceedingly blue,
"It bores me, you know, to walk to and fro,
I'll reverse it and walk fro and to."

There is one painfully suggestive of that lowest
form of wit, the pun:

There was a young farmer named Hall,
Who fell in the spring in the fall;
'Twould have been a sad thing
If he fell in the spring,
But he didn't; he fell in the fall.

This is cleverly reflective of, let us say, modern
fashions:

> There was a young girl at the shore,
> Looked the same from behind as before.
>   You never knew where
>   To offer a chair,
> So she had to sit down on the floor.

VIII

Just with a little twist to it is this one:

> There was a young girl named Bianca,
> Who retired while the ship was at anchor,
> But awoke, with dismay,
> When she heard the mate say:
> "We must pull up the top sheet and spanker."

This play on a name is perhaps the best in the
limerick realm:

> There was an od fellow in Tyre
> Who constantly sat on the fire.
> When asked "Is it hot?"
> He replied "No, it's not;
> I'm James Winterbottom, Esquire."

There is the same attempt here:

> A girl whose name it was Ounce,
> Used language I will not pronounce.
> Her brother, one day,
> Pulled her chair right away,
> He wanted to see if she'd bounce.

Again here:

> There was an old lady named Worcester
> Who vowed that no man had e'er kissed her.
> But her chin and her nose
> Grew together so close
> If any man tried he'd have missed her.

IX

This limerick often cited by Woodrow Wilson was really not from his pen at all. It is by Anthony Euwer, but Mr. Wilson liked it, and would often quote it as applied to his own appearance:

> As a beauty I am not a star,
> There are others more handsome by far,
> But my face—I don't mind it
> For I am behind it,
> It's the people in front get the jar.

A clever paraphrase on a proper name is this famous rhyming bit:

> There was an old man of Nantucket,
> Who kept all his cash in a bucket,
> But his daughter, named Nan,
> Ran away with a man,
> And as for the bucket—Nantucket!

"One of the cleverest," says a limerick authority:

> An epicure, dining at Lou,
> Found quite a large mouse in his stew.

> Said the waiter, "Don't shout,
> And wave it about,
> Or the rest will be wanting one, too."

This, too, is from England, where the limerick seems to be prevalent:

> There was a fat lady of Harrow
> Who rode into church in a barrow.
> When she stuck in the aisle
> She said with a smile,
> "They build these 'ere churches too narrow."

A young priest adopted the recent fad of "eating a cake of yeast a day," and one morning found this in his mail:

> There once was a pious young priest
> Who lived almost wholly on yeast,
> "For," he said, "it is plain
> We must all rise again,
> And I want to get started, at least."

X

Of course, this is an old favorite, but always popular:

> There was a young girl of Nantucket,
> With a bustle as big as a bucket,
> She filled it with oats
> And the bad billy-goats
> Came right up behind her an' tucket.

Something akin is this one less known:

> There was a young lady of Cheadle
> Who sat down in a church on a needle.
> Though deeply imbedded
> 'Twas luckily threaded,
> So she had it drawn out by the beadle.

Here is what is called a masterpiece of significant English syllables making natural words:

> A reticent fellow named Tate
> Took his girl out to dine at eight eight.
> As Tate does not state,
> I cannot relate
> What Tate and his tête-à-tête ate at eight eight.

Somewhat on the same line of syllable combinations is this:

> A tutor who tooted a flute,
> Tried to teach two young tutors to toot.
> Said the two to the tutor:
> "Is it harder to toot, or
> To tutor two tutors to toot?"

Oliver Herford is said to be author of this one:

> There's a lady in Kalamazoo
> Who bites all her oysters in two;
> For she has a misgiving
> If any were living,
> They'd kick up a hullabaloo!

Along a similar line is this:

> A fly and a flea in a flue
> Were imprisoned, so what could they do?
> Said the fly, "Let us flee!"
> "Let us fly," said the flea.
> So they flew through a flaw in the flue.

XI

Of course, the fair-sex is a sweet morsel for the limerickist. This one differs from many:

> There was a young lady named Sis,
> Who said, "I think roller-skating just bliss."
> This no more will she state
> For a wheel off her skate
> Made her finish up something like this.

This one came from the country:

> There was a young lady called Bitee
> Whom the women declared to be flighty,
> For if Monday were fine
> They would see, on her line,
> A shocking diaphanous nightee.

Unkindly in a sense is this:

> There was an old maid of Vancouver
> Who captured a man by manœuvre
> When she jumped on his knee,
> Called the household to see,
> And nothing on earth could remove her.

Famous and clever is this:

> There was a young girl of Asburias,
> Whose temper was frantic and furious.
> She used to throw eggs
> At her grandmother's legs,
> A habit unpleasant, but curious.

Why folks in Maine should love this one I don't know, but they do I am told:

> There was a young lady of Maine
> Who was fearfully sick on the train
> Not once, but again
> And again and again
> And again and again and AGAIN.

XII

This certainly is full of imagination:

> There was a young lady named Anna,
> Who in church sang the highest soprano,
> When she fell on the stair
> The tenor said, "There,
> I've heard, now I've seen your Hoseanna!"

Likewise this:

> There was a young lady of Erskin
> Who had the most beautiful fair skin.
> When I said to her, "Mable,
> You look well in your sable,"
> She replied, "I look best in my bearskin."

XIII

Just at this point, my wife, reading these, and after having read this last one, remarked: "I think that will do."

Perhaps she's right!

CHAPTER TEN

A HAPPY GROUP OF EIGHT

"I want you to drop in just for a few moments with me at the Babcocks'," said The Lady to me one day as we were driving home.

"Isn't that more for women?" I meekly ventured.

"Oh, no," was the assurance. "Mr. Babcock will be home, and you can talk men's stuff to him."

And as Babcock was my banker, I took courage.

CHAPTER TEN

A HAPPY GROUP OF EIGHT

I

BABCOCK was not at home. He had just left for the club, his wife explained.

The wily husband had scented the battle.

For I found that we had fallen both-footedly into a group of women who were having a fast and furious discussion of the servant question. The idea of my "sitting in" seemed to give new zest to the group. At it they went.

It was curious how they seemed to enjoy it. They actually relished it! I never saw a company of women apparently so happy, and yet they were all aggrieved.

II

Every woman of the eight—save two—was full of domestic grievances: sure of the conviction that mistresses had no rights and that it was growing increasingly impossible to keep house: hence the rush toward apartment-houses. It was a recital of hiring and firing and hiring and leaving; more of leaving, as I figured it, than of firing. Servants remained a week, a fort-

night or a month. Then some morning they were not,
—particularly the morning after pay-day.

The two silent women interested me. One was my
wife. I signalled to her to wade in. But wade in she
would not, and did not. Not a stroke! It was explained to me afterward that her experience, which
was entirely different from those recited, would not
have been popular: in fact, I was assured that it
would have infuriated all except the other silent
woman. This other silent woman, however, was not
so circumspect. She was a young woman who I was
soon to find out had more intelligence and discernment than all the other six women present. I noticed,
too, that the other women—from an acknowledged in-
feriority-complex, it struck me—listened attentively
to her. "For two years I had the troubles you all
have had," she began very quietly. "I could afford
only one girl, but not one could I keep longer than
three months: most of them three weeks. Then they
departed with every kind of an excuse save what
I felt to be the true one. It was not her room, because it was really a large, bright room and the maid
had a bath of her own. I decided to find out myself
the seat of the trouble. So when the last girl left, instead of employing another I decided to do the work
myself: take care of all our seven rooms and our four
children. It was a day's work, but I did it for three
months. I found out that I had asked and expected

too much of a single girl: not only was the work
heavy: it was practically impossible to get it done—
done well as I wished it to be done. Then I engaged
another girl: had a woman-cleaner come in once a
week and gave out the laundry. As it was, the girl's
day was full. Now I can afford two girls, and every
hour of their days is full. The first girl I have had
seven years: the other five. Each knows that I know
her work, and I find that fact to count for much."

A dead silence fell on the group. The complainers
had been silenced and unpleasantly convinced. Not
one, I was credibly informed afterward, could have
done her own work.

III

I could plainly see that the speaker was not wildly
popular with that group. Women are most self-
revealing when they think they are most impene-
trable.

Then as a parting thought there came from this
wise young woman: "Running a house and servants
is as much of a science as anything else. It is really
an art, essentially a feminine one, and the problem is
not solved by women running away from it and
dragging their husbands and children into the modern
homeless apartment-house or hotel (that was really a
nasty one, because three of the women had done that
very thing!) I cannot help feeling that if women

would cease their mad rush into politics and civics (this little sally covered two others), which they were not created to understand and cannot grasp, and devote themselves to solving the problem of housekeeping, which is essentially theirs, and playing true with their husbands and children, the domestic machinery of scores of homes would run more smoothly and women would be doing the work for which they were created and are fitted to do. I used to play around with civics, and delude myself into believing that I was getting somewhere with the tax problem, our immigration restrictions, our foreign relations, but I was constantly discovering, the more I went into these problems, that each was a life study of itself and at the best that the knowledge I sought to get at meetings and conventions was not only superficial, but usually partisan, with the information almost invariably wrong—particularly at the so-called 'current events' classes."

IV

I wondered what would happen in that little party where six of the eight women had been so neatly ticketed, and where I could see the claws were good and ready!

"Do you vote?" finally ventured one of the group, with an ill-feigned meekness.

"I certainly do," was the answer.

"How do you know whom to vote for?" came next.

"By the same method followed by every woman I know: by listening to my husband and voting as he votes."

This time every woman smiled! But they also unanimously agreed that it was time to go home. And every woman assured the hostess that she had "*such a delightful time!*"

The perplexing part of it is that I think they did!

CHAPTER ELEVEN

IN WHICH SOME FAMOUS NAMES OCCUR

I have said on a previous page that in my business life I did not have the opportunity of meeting any of the national figures in American life. I should qualify this with an exception or two which, until now, I had overlooked.

CHAPTER ELEVEN

IN WHICH SOME FAMOUS NAMES OCCUR

I

SOME years ago I felt pretty well frayed at the edges, and The Lady persuaded me to take three weeks off and go on a trip to Bermuda. There was prospect of a piece of business there coming our way, so I gave my conscience a sop by the feeling that I could combine business with pleasure.

II

On the boat we found that Mark Twain was on board, and when it came to our first meal we found ourselves seated at the same table. The captain introduced us, and as I took a fancy to the humorist I cultivated his acquaintance.

The voyage was, as voyages to Bermuda are apt to be, pretty rough, and as Mark Twain was not a good sailor, he had a bad time of it. He stuck to the deck and, "to save walking," as he termed it, he habitually leaned over the rail. I was standing by when the deck steward came up and, trying to hand Mark a cup of soup, said: "I thought I'd just bring you a little something to eat up here on deck, Mr. Twain, and save you the trouble of coming down."

The humorist looked at the soup and the steward, and then: "Thanks, steward, you could save me a little more trouble if you'd throw the soup over the rail."

"Is there anything I *can* bring you, sir?" persisted the steward.

"Yes, steward," returned Mark, perking up, "bring me a nice, good-sized island."

Just then Albert Bigelow Payne, who was travelling with the humorist, came up and said to him: "Really, you ought to come over on the other side and see a four-master with full sails set passing by."

Mark looked at his friend, and said dismally: "You can have the damned ship. Come and tell me when you see some trees passing by."

"You don't like the water?" I ventured.

"Like it?" he growled. "What is there to like about it?" and then, never forgetting the humorous side of a situation, he added grimly: "I am kept too damned busy on ship-board with my six meals."

"Six?" I echoed.

"Yes," returned Mark. "Three down and three up."

"There's only one thing to take on ship-board," he added.

"What is that?" I asked.

"Blackberry brandy," returned Mark. "It tastes the same both ways."

III

Earlier in my life I had been fond of hunting, and as a vacation after my college graduation I went after some big game in the Rockies. Of course, I had my experiences, as has every man who has gone after the grizzly, which had been my goal. My experiences were retailed by a friend to Theodore Roosevelt. To my amazement, years later, when he was visiting in the city where I then lived, he sent word that he would like to have me invited and placed next to him at the dinner to be given him, so that we "might talk Rockies."

IV

I went, and found myself placed next to the Colonel at the head-table. It was at the time when there was a deal of talk about Colonel Roosevelt's alcoholic drinking, which finally resulted in the famous suit against a Western editor. Just below us there was seated a friend of mine whose investments had been lessened in value by the Colonel's stand against trusts, and he never forgave him. It was the sure signal for an outburst of wrath to mention the Colonel's name in his presence. Why he was present at this dinner, where he would have to listen to the Colonel speak, I don't know. But he was there, and I noticed his eyes scarcely left the Colonel.

Then, the reason for his riveted attention upon the
Colonel became clear to me.

During the dinner the Colonel had served to him
glass after glass of a drink which sparkled. The bottle
had been wrapped in a towel. He was in an excellent
frame of mind, because he had lived over his days in
the Rockies with me, and when he rose to speak he was
in fine fettle. This was my friend's opportunity: he
lost no time to couple the Colonel's happy frame of
mind with the contents of the bottle, and what was
simpler or easier than a graphic recital of the many
glasses of champagne which the Colonel imbibed and
his rollicking speech? My friend had a wonderful
time with that story. He still has, although he knows
there is not a word of truth in his version of it.

So, at an opportune moment, I said to the Colonel:
"Mind if I have a glass of your sparkle?"

"Sure," he said. "But don't take too much. It's
heady, you know," he added with a grin.

My friend heard this pleasantry, and his eyes
lighted up.

When the waiter had filled my glass, I took the
bottle, unfolded the towel so that I could see the label
and turned the label to my friend to read. The waiter
explained: "Sparkling White Rock, sir."

But with my friend it was champagne, and champagne it still is to-day. He saw my glass poured, he
knew I never drank alcohol, he saw the label, as he

afterward told me. But the story, as he tells it, still deals with "glass after glass of champagne."

But "wot'ell," as Chimmie Fadden used to say!

V

Speaking of Theodore Roosevelt, I am, naturally, finding more time to read in these days of my retirement. The other evening while reading Oliver's *Life of Alexander Hamilton*, I came across this passage which it seems to me is about as excellent an epitome of Theodore Roosevelt as it is of Hamilton:

"To pretend that he (Hamilton) had no joy in battle, no exultation in victory, would be absurd, for his nature was frank and vehement. He was never detached and seldom reticent. To endure human folly in patient and hopeful expectation of the inevitable reaction was contrary to his character. He had no hatred of limelight nor horror of applause, but both with him were secondary matters. Throughout his whole life the paramount motive was to get things done, not to make himself a great fame by doing things. So unusual an ambition has caused him to be suspected of an inordinate subtlety. To the common politician whose main sincerity is his determination to ride into popular notice on the back of a grievance or a fit of hysterics, such an attitude is wholly incredible. He cannot fathom the depths of a spirit that loves union and order and progress for their own sakes, and seeks power, not as an end to itself, but as a means to the accomplishment of a vision. And yet, to the candid reader of Hamilton's life and writings, nothing is clearer at every turn than that he came to enact his high and notable part in public affairs chiefly because it seemed to be the only way open to him of getting the work done which he considered essential for the salvation of his adopted country."

Just a deletion here and there, and the picture of Alexander Hamilton—respected of all to-day—fits the personality of Theodore Roosevelt—respected of all to-morrow.

It is all a question of to-morrow!

VI

It was at the dinner to which I referred a paragraph back that I told the Colonel of a discussion which had arisen over the correct pronunciation of the first syllable of his name—whether it should be pronounced like "moose" or like the rose-flower.

"Like a rose," he promptly answered. "It is Dutch, you know: Roose-velt—the English of 'velt' is field. I suspect there was once an 'n' between the syllables, but as the 'n' at the end of a word in Dutch is silent, it came to be spelled as it is. No, it is as if it were spelled 'rose.' "

VII

At the family table the following evening, when I triumphantly repeated the Colonel's explanation of his name (for I had stood out for "rose" against the family), we fell to talking about names, and a friend who was present surprised the table by saying that Robert Louis Stevenson's name was really Lewis Balfour Stevenson, and that a letter addressed by a friend to Lewis B. Stevenson, in care of his English publishers, was returned to him with the comment "Party unknown at address given." A similar case was that when a letter addressed to Thomas W. Wilson during Woodrow Wilson's Presidency was returned to the Washington Post-Office by some White House official with "No such party" written across the face of the envelope. At the lyceum Theatre, in London, during Sir Henry Irving's occupancy of the theatre, a letter addressed to John Henry Brodribb was returned to the sender. And, in America, a family letter addressed to Miss M. Kiskadden to the theatre where Maud Adams was playing was refused and returned. This also happened when a letter addressed to Miss Sarah Frances Frost was refused at the theatre where Julia Marlowe was playing. Madame Melba's father had returned to him a letter written to his daughter addressed at a concert-hall where she was singing, because he sent it to Miss Nellie Mitchell

Armstrong. Sarah Bernhardt's husband had the same experience when he addressed his wife as Madame Damala at her Paris theatre, and it is altogether likely that a letter addressed to Rosine Bernard (her real name) would have met the same fate.

VIII

Speaking of Robert Louis Stevenson, that must have been a delicious moment when Sir James M. Barrie told his famous story of his only meeting with Stevenson. No record of this wonderful story has, so far as I have read, been made in anything save the newspapers of the following day, so I venture to give it this more lasting form.

Barrie said that the only time he ever met Stevenson was in the winter of 1879. "I well remember it," was the way Barrie told it, "because the wind was 'blawin' snell' when I set off that afternoon with my note-books to the Humanities class of the University of Edinburgh. As I was crossing Princes-street—a blasty corner—I ran against another wayfarer. Looking up, I saw that he was a young man of an exceeding tenuity of body, his eyes, his hair, already beginning to go black, and that he was wearing a velvet jacket. He passed on, but he had bumped against me, and I stood in the middle of the street, regardless of the traffic, and glared contemptuously after him.

"He must have grown conscious of this, because he

turned around and looked at me. I continued to glare. He went on a bit, and turned around again. I was still glaring, and he came back and said to me, quite nicely: 'After all, God made me.'

"I said: 'He is getting careless.'

"He lifted his cane, and then, instead, he said: 'Do I know you?'

"He said it with such extraordinary charm that I replied, wistfully: 'No, but I wish you did.'

"He said: 'Let's pretend I do,' and we went off to a tavern at the foot of Leith-street, where we drank what he said was the favorite wine of the Three Musketeers. Each of us wanted to pay, but it did not much matter, as neither of us had any money.

"We had to leave that tavern without the velvet coat and without my class books. When we got out it was snowing hard, and we quarrelled—something about Mary Queen of Scots. I remember how he chased me for hours that snowy night through the streets of Edinburgh, calling for my blood."

The mere fact that Stevenson was not in Edinburgh at all in 1879, and that not a word of the anecdote is true, does not take away from it the delicious "spoofing" quality of Barrie.

IX

It may be due to my rather restricted reading (although, to my mind, I have read widely during the past year), but I can find nowhere in any book an incident which I feel should have a more permanent record.

The story is that an American author found in his mail one morning a letter enclosing some unusual data. He acknowledged the letter to a temporary stenographer, who destroyed her note-books and the letter and data. The data was written on the leaves of an ordinary note-book. The sender told that he was the grandson of the circuit preacher referred to; that he had found these fragmentary and undated leaves among his grandfather's papers, and ventured to send them to the author, saying that as he himself was not a writer he hoped they might prove of some interest to him, and that he might make use of them. The data seemed improbable and yet, on second thought, told of an incident that might very well have happened. The discolored note-book leaves on which the happening was told certainly bore every trace of age, and there was absolutely no reason to doubt the authenticity of the material.

X

The incident told of a Southern circuit preacher who had ended his long day of riding and visitation at a cabin in a clearing where a woman and her son sat under a candle-light poring over a book at a rough wooden table. The father of the family was away over the night; the preacher's visit was particularly welcome. And, after a frugal meal, the trio sat around the table with the flickering candles under which the boy kept pondering over his book, with his finger laboriously pointing at the words. "He is learning to read," said the woman in explanation. "The chances here are so meagre. We must make the most of what we can get."

"But we know that the potentialities in a life are great nowadays, no matter what the surroundings," said the preacher.

The boy looked up. "What was that word?" he asked.

"Word?" echoed the preacher.

"Yes," answered the boy, "you said po—— something."

"Oh! Potentialities," smiled the preacher.

"Yes; what does it mean? asked the boy.

XI

"Potentialities, my boy, mean the possibilities in our lives; there is something potential, something inherently possible in each of us."

"In each of us?" came the eager question.

"Yes, in each life, no matter how humble. The lives of all great men teach us that. What is that book you are reading?" asked the man of the circuit.

"Trying to read," corrected the boy with just the

flicker of a smile. "It is called *Great Thoughts by Great Men*."

"And what thought were you reading?" kindly asked the preacher.

"It says," the boy read slowly, " 'Every great' "— "movement," broke in the woman—" 'movement,' " repeated the boy, " 'is begun by one man.' "

"That is true, very true," said the preacher.

"But it says nothing about his ending it," said the boy, looking up inquiringly at the preacher.

"That is given to very few, my boy," was the answer. "Very few are allowed to finish what they begin. We work in one generation to serve another. The man who plants the acorn rarely sees the full-grown oak."

"I shouldn't like to begin what I couldn't end," philosophized the boy, and then he added: "But I guess I'll never have a chance to begin anything— here." And with his head resting between his hands and his elbows on the table, he motioned with a side nod to the world outside.

XII

The woman looked up and, laying her hand on the head of the boy and lovingly running her fingers through the shock of black hair, said: "I am not so sure of that. Sometimes I feel as if you——"

And then the fingers stopped, and the mother

looked over the boy's head into the darkness of the cabin beyond. Fixedly she gazed until the preacher saw a light come in the woman's eyes such as he had never seen before in one of God's children. Instinctively he turned and followed her look into the dark recesses of the room. The boy looked up into the woman's face, her hand resting quietly on his head. There was not a movement of the body as she stared with a wondrous light as of heaven in those eyes. What was the mother seeing in that darkness that the man of God could not see? What vision is it that comes to a mother at such a time, when the soul of motherhood peers into the future of her child and tries to pierce the years ahead? Is there a vision of motherhood that is denied to others? Is a mother privileged to enter into a sphere not of mortals at such a time? Is she given a glimpse into the Divine Will in a spiritual vista that is only for her? Who will say or deny what God vouchsafes to a mother in moments of intense spiritual anxiety when the future of that which she has received from God's hand is deep in her soul?

Seconds only they were, but minutes they seemed to the onlookers as the woman continued to gaze into the spaces beyond. She seemed, as the preacher looked at her, as if she had been transported to another plane; as if there sat before him one who was treading the realms of which he had so often preached.

Not a breath seemed to leave the body; not a motion was there. Then, in an instant, there flashed a look of fear as can only come into a mother's eyes; even the flickering candle-light revealed the blanched face of the woman as she convulsively grasped the boy's head between her hands, and, with a sob of distress that pierced the soul of the preacher, cried in a voice of deep appeal, "No, no, dear God; not that, dear God!"

The preacher sat mute as if divine visitation was upon him. The boy clutched at his mother.

"What is it, mother, what is it?"

XIII

With a sigh that seemed to come from the very depth of her soul, and with a bewildered glance at the preacher and the boy as if she had returned to them from another world, her hands dropped from the boy's head and, putting them over her eyes as if to wipe out a vision, she gave a wan smile and answered, exhausted: "Nothing, dear, nothing."

Then, collecting herself, and taking one of the three candles from the table, she arose: "Come, we should all go to bed."

XIV

And, with the preacher rising as if in a trance, and the wondering boy still looking at his mother, she leaned down, gazed for a moment deep into the boy's eyes and, tilting the lad's face downward, she almost buried her face in the dark hair as she imprinted the long, tender kiss of a mother on the head of Abraham Lincoln.

AUTHOR'S NOTE. Lord Charnwood in his wonderful "Life of Lincoln" says, on page 6: "Sarah Bush Lincoln, his stepmother, was good to him, and he to her. Above all she encouraged him in his early studies, to which a fretful housewife could have opposed such terrible obstacles. She lived to hope that he might not be elected President for fear that enemies should kill him, and she lived to have her fear fulfilled," from which it may reasonably be surmised that the woman in the foregoing incident was Lincoln's stepmother.

CHAPTER TWELVE
SAFETY FIRST

"Writing a book, are you?" said a friend to me recently. "Well, if you have room for it, put in a story I'll tell you. It has never been published, and has a lot in it for a lot of men,—particularly young men."

"All right," I agreed, and the story is on the following page.

CHAPTER TWELVE
SAFETY FIRST

I

THE story was of a day, some years ago, when every lawyer and legal firm in the Northwest were taken by surprise when the railroad interests representing the investments of James J. Hill announced that the most important railroad suit of a decade was to be handled, for the Hill interests, not by the regular firm retained as counsel by Hill for all his court work, but by a comparatively unknown firm, one of whose members was named Spear.

Naturally, the most surprised of all was the regular counsel, whose senior member at once sought the great railroad magnate.

"Of course," said the lawyer to Mr. Hill, "we concede at once that it is your privilege to engage any legal firm you like. But naturally the announcement that the firm you have selected is to handle this important case makes us wonder whether anything has happened to make you dissatisfied with us."

"Not dissatisfied, exactly," returned Hill. "Just a case of a greater confidence in Spear. He won the Piermont case against us, you remember, three years ago."

"Yes," remembered the lawyer, "but that was be-cause the breaks in the case happened to be with him."

"No," returned Hill. "That's where you are wrong," and then the railroad builder made the sage remark so often quoted from him. "Nothing ever just happens. Everything is brought about. You brought that about yourself."

"How so?" asked the lawyer.

"Do you remember the evening before the case came up, when we were all at the Auditorium, and after dinner while we were in a group talking, Spear happened by and you hailed him and asked if he didn't want to join you and two others in a poker hand in your room?"

"Just hazily," answered the lawyer, wondering what was coming.

"Well, I do," said Hill, "very clearly. I can see young Spear now as he answered: 'No, thanks. I generally get a long night before a big day,' and you assured him that he was to have 'a big day all right.' He smiled, went up-stairs, and by nine-thirty he had switched off his light and was asleep. You and your partners went up and played poker until two A. M. That distribution of night life went on during the two weeks' trial, and Spear showed his method in his trial-work and you showed your method in your trial-work."

The lawyer was quiet.

"There were no 'breaks,' as you call them, in the trial for Spear: not one," continued Hill. "It was simply a case of Spear getting his long nights of sleep and leaving two A. M. poker parties to our counsel. His mind worked beautifully: yours lagged. The result of the case lay in that contrast. It was perfectly evident to me throughout the trial. I knew we would lose. I have watched Spear ever since, and have waited two years for a real stiff case to come along, so that I might give it to him. I can't afford to let two A. M. poker games lose my big suits for me."

II

It was this same James J. Hill who put the question of thrift in money matters with epigrammatic force when he said that he could tell of any man at twenty-five whether he would be worth a nickel at fifty.

"How?" asked a friend.

"All I want to see is his bank-account," returned Hill. "If he has a good account at twenty-five, he will be all right at fifty. If he hasn't, he won't. I have never known it to fail."

"The trouble is that this is a very difficult truth for some young men at twenty-five to grasp," said the friend.

"I did," was the laconic answer.

III

Of course, every young man at twenty-five is not an embryonic James J. Hill. The unescapable truth is there, however. It is fundamental. It was this great railroad king who also said that if there existed a secret in success, it lay in thrift. It is too often said that thrift in youth makes a miser in old age, but for every miser that thrift has made it has made a hundred men where a competence has come. No general rule is always true, but there are few exceptions to the rule that where a man is a spendthrift with his own money he is most unlikely to be careful of the money of others. And that is the rung of the ladder of business success on which a young man must be able to stand firmly before he can climb to the next rung. He may have every possible natural endowment for affairs, but, lacking thrift for himself and for others, he will not reach achievement. The vitality of a great business lies not so much in its income as in its outgo. Many a large income business has been wrecked by wasteful expense in small items. It is the eye trained to the left side of the ledger that is the most valuable factor in the business. A man cannot acquire that in later years. It must be with him and of him from the beginning: when he is a young man. And the habit starts with his own affairs: what his own bank-account says at twenty-five!

IV

The stiffest lot of figures about any hundred average American men ever put into print was in an article called "What Happens to 100 Average Men?" Stiff as is the showing given, the article, published years ago, has outlived any article on the subject, and during all the years that have gone by, its truth has never been successfully questioned. The strength of the article rests on the fact that it was the result of the most careful and direct investigation into the lives of thousands of men. It was based on actual cases. It showed that out of every 100 young fellows who started, 36 passed away at or before 65, the majority from physical or moral excesses. Only a few passed away from natural causes. That left 64 to be accounted for. Fifty-seven of these 64 were shown as being either supported by relatives, in the poor-houses, or in actual want. That left 7. Of these 7, 4 were comfortably off: 2 were well-off and 1 was rich. Rather chilly figures, you say. Yes, but "there's a reason." The investigators showed that all the latter 7 who were either comfortably fixed, well-off or rich—without exception, they were the thrifty ones from young manhood up, and that not 1 of the 57 who had failed had ever thought of saving. They had lived either up to their incomes or beyond.

The conclusion to be drawn from what may seem staggering figures is perfectly simple: when a young man learns the vital lesson of thrift, thrift not only in money matters but in his habits and hours, he learns the lessons of the 7 in every 100. That does not mean that he must deprive himself of good times while he is young. It is simply that good times do not consist of wild-oats, but in a moderate and rightful thrift of pleasures and hours. Moderation and care. That is all.

V

I was reminded of this the other day by a man who has made a large mark in American life. I noticed that all through our talk he kept smelling of the cigar which I gave him, but did not smoke it.

"Dry-smoking these days?" I queried.

"Yes, not these days, but always," he replied.

"How is that?" I asked.

"Well," he answered, "I make my eight hours' work a day my chief concern in life, and I train for it just as an athlete does for a contest. I love tobacco, for instance, but I never smoke. I am fond of alcohol, but I never drink. I drink from six to eight tumblers of water a day. I am devoted to the good things of the table, but I eat sparingly and only twice a day. I like to sit up with the rest of them at night, but I go to bed early so as to get from eight to ten hours' sleep."

"And the result?" I asked.

"I am never sick," was the reply. "Every morning finds me keen for my work."

"And you think it is worth it?" I persisted.

"I do," was the answer. "Not only for what I am doing, but for what I mean to do."

"What is that?" I ventured.

"I am going to retire in about five years, just as you have done. Then, with the personal responsibility of my affairs removed, I am going to smoke in moderation, indulge my love of reading before I go to sleep, and go in for civics."

All of which explains what scores of this man's friends and associates have wondered at: the uniformly good health of this recognized master of industry; always fit; always ready for the day's work.

An excellent illustration is this that thrift means something else than the careful husbanding of money.

VI

The most remarkable instance of thrift with time is the case of the chauffeur of a friend. I chanced to hear him speak an unusually good English. Then, about a month later, my ear caught him speaking French to a governess.

"You are French?" I asked.

"Oh, no, sir," he laughingly replied. "I was born in Canton, Ohio."

I wondered, and then when yesterday I heard him

speak in German to a policeman, I could not help saying to him: "You are quite a linguist."

"Hardly that," he smiled back at me.

"But I have heard you speak three languages," I persisted.

"Brokenly," he replied. "But I practise it wherever I can. I had an hour in Italian with a hotel waiter this morning, and it helped considerably." And tucked away in his pocket I saw the top of an Italian grammar.

I was now thoroughly interested, and asked: "What is your idea in learning these languages?"

"Oh, just a way of filling up my leisure hours. You see, sir, a chauffeur has more leisure than anything else. My hours are from eight in the morning until I am through at night. On an average I am either on call or waiting from five to six hours a day. That is too much to waste, and I have used my leisure during the six years I have been with Mr. Nelson to learn my own language and these three others. I started out with the idea of one language a year, but haven't quite made that record."

"How do you go about it?" I inquired.

"Well, sir," was the surprising reply, "I had very little schooling, and so I thought I would first get an idea of my own language. So I bought a dictionary, a grammar, and a phrase book, or a book of synonyms. Then when I felt I had about learned all I could comfortably hold, I bought a copy of Trevelyan's *Civil War*, Bryce's *Commonwealth*, and Woodrow Wilson's *History of the American People.* Combined, that gave me a fair idea of the English language and of American history."

"Then how did you go about learning the foreign languages?" I asked.

"The same way, sir," was the reply. "I tackled German next. Bought a grammar, an English and German dictionary, a German glossary of words, and then I read three volumes of German history. The same with French, and now I am mid-channel in Italian."

"What after that?" I ventured.

"Spanish rather attracts me," was the nonchalant answer, and then, almost apologetically: "It is just using up waiting time, that's all."

"What are you going to do with all this knowledge?" I asked.

"Well, sir," he answered with a smile, "I would hardly call it knowledge. Rather a smatter. I don't know, sir, how to answer your question. I don't think it would get me any farther than driving a car, and I know that pretty well. I have just been amusing myself really. It is like taking Mr. and Mrs. Nelson to the opera. I got interested, and bought a copy of *The Stories of the Opera.* I thought I would like to know what the operas are all about. I have never seen

an opera, but if I take Mr. and Mrs. Nelson to hear
Faust, for example, I take my book along, and while
they are inside listening to the opera I am reading
about it. Just curiosity, I suppose. I like to know why
people are interested in things and what these things
are. I am not musical, and probably I shouldn't enjoy such a long evening of opera if I heard one. But
I know what it is all about, and I think I will let it
go at that. Last winter Mr. and Mrs. Nelson went
three times to hear *Hamlet*, and so I got a one-volume
edition of Shakespeare, read *Hamlet*, liked it immensely,
and then on my first evening off I went to see John
Barrymore play it."

"Did you like it?" I ventured.

"Ye-es, sir," he answered doubtfully. "But to me
it read better than it sounded. I read it again the
next day. Perhaps you have to hear it more than
once. That may be why Mr. and Mrs. Nelson went
three times."

VII

Never had I met with a more remarkable illustration of thrift as applied to time which thousands of
other men, equally situated, wasted. But I realize
that the case is exceptional. I wondered what use he
would make of his knowledge. Then I sought a chance
to sit beside him in the car.

"How old are you, Dickson?" I asked.

CHAPTER THIRTEEN

A STEAMSHIP AND A COW

I have friends who the moment Mr. Bok's name is mentioned break out into the most delicious merriment for his outline of the American institutions of Dutch origin. What these merry individuals overlook, however, is that Mr. Bok does not make these claims. It is History they should laugh at, for it is History that has recorded them. Nor has Mr. Bok ever made his list complete.

"Twenty-nine, sir."

"Married."

"Not yet, sir," with a most expansive smile.

"In the offing, is it?" I inquired.

"Very close," was the instant answer. "Then," he added, "if I have a family I am going to see to it that my children begin earlier, and—" He hesitated as just a suggestion of a shadow swept over his genial face.

"What?" I asked gently.

"Get somewhere, sir."

That, then, was the secret tucked away in the heart of this far-seeing chauffeur! His children would benefit by the use of the father's "waits"!

CHAPTER THIRTEEN
A STEAMSHIP AND A COW

I

TAKE the question of the first American steamship to cross the Atlantic Ocean. American historians have for years coddled themselves with the belief that this achievement belonged to the *Savannah*, which, in 1819, is supposed to have been the pioneer vessel to cross the Atlantic propelled by steam. This is true, in a measure, but not in whole. The *Savannah* did cross the Atlantic, sailing from Savannah, Georgia, for Saint Petersburg, via London. It took her twenty-nine days to make the voyage. But of this trip of nearly a month she used her steam just eighty hours. It was enough to demonstrate the feasibility of steam power, but one can hardly claim that this was a steam crossing. They had an interesting custom on the *Savannah* of taking "her wheels in on deck," which they did "in thirty minutes," according to the captain's log. On her return voyage to Savannah, she did not use her steam power at all. "Fuel was too high," wrote the captain. But even with this obstacle removed, she could not have made the voyage

by steam because her builders declared that her
limit of fuel capacity was seventy-five tons of coal and
twenty-five cords of wood—hardly enough fuel to
propel a three-hundred-ton vessel for twenty-nine
days!

The Canadians have come along and said that
the steamer *Royal William* was, in 1831, the first
Atlantic steam-liner. She depended entirely on her
machinery for propelling purposes. But this, mark
you, was in the latter part of 1831. She was the first
British steamer, yes——

But in 1826 there was sold by its British builders
to the Dutch Government a vessel called *Calpe*, which
name the Dutch, upon purchase, changed to *Curacao*.
She had "2 engines of 50-horse power (nominal)
each." On April 27, 1831, she made her maiden trip
across the Atlantic. But she made her entire crossing by steam. Each year thereafter she made a round
Atlantic trip, and always she depended upon her
steam power and machinery.

It may be asked why it is that successive histories
of steam-navigation are silent on this question of the
Curacao. Perhaps the answer to this is that these
histories were written by American and English authorities whose visions have naturally been filled with
pictures of the *Savannah* and the *Royal William*.
Which is not so unnatural!

II

Take another instance.

Again, like Mr. Bok, I am not saying this: I am simply recording the recorder.

The speaker here is the Honorable Frank O. Lowden, whose word is certainly respected throughout America; who, while Governor of Illinois and since, has had one of the finest herds of dairy cattle in the country: himself an expert when it comes to the cow.

He—not I, remember—claims and proves it: that the finest of American dairy cattle are to-day descended from what we call the Holstein-Friesian cow. Of course, everybody knows, who knows anything about dairy cattle, that the cow in the Province of Friesland, in the Netherlands, is the superior cow of the world. But these marvellous cows have not remained in Friesland. As Mr. Lowden tells me, these cows have literally gone around the world and a large majority of all the best dairy cattle in the United States are of this breed. In South Africa, too, he says they have made a conquest, and in South America they outrank cows of all other breeds in popularity. Not only that, says my informant, but within the last few years the black and white Friesian type, the blanket cow as it is called, has threatened the supremacy of the best British breeds in the British Isles. Mr. Lowden says he knows of no other domestic ani-

mal of any particular breed whose conquest has been
so world-wide, and when, as the dairy-Governor says,
one considers the vital importance of the cow in relation to human health and progress, this Dutch
achievement is vitally important.

So, the first Atlantic liner and the best cow must
be added to the public schools, golf, the Constitution
of the United States and the score and two of other
distinctly American achievements which, as a matter
of history, are of Dutch initiative and Dutch origin!

Not as a claim, but as a record.

PART II

CHAPTER FOURTEEN

THE QUIET SILENT STRENGTH OF
ENGLAND

"You've done very well these two months or so," said The Man of Medicine one day to me. "Now, I want you to make a complete break with the past this spring and summer. How about going across?"

"Across?" I echoed.

"Yes, England say. Go and see England in May. Wonderful time to see her highways of May. Go and saunter along the Devonshire and Cornwall coasts, and then to the Lake country. Say for three or four months. You'll come back feeling all made over. It will give you a complete change, new impressions, and broaden you a heap."

"It doesn't sound badly," I commented.

"Badly? Is that the best you can say for it? Wish I were the lucky pup you are, to be able to go. Let me see you out of here in a fortnight," was his parting greeting.

And in a fortnight we *were* "out of here."

CHAPTER FOURTEEN
THE QUIET SILENT STRENGTH
OF ENGLAND

I

WE arrived plumb in the great strike of May, 1926. All the taxis in Southampton were out of commission.

"Where do you wish to go, sir?" asked a voice at my side as we stood helpless on the dock.

"London, if we can get there," was my answer.

"Quite all right, sir," was the cheerful reply. "I have a car, and will take you there. I am a volunteer, you know, sir."

And, excellently driven, we arrived in London.

"Nothing at all, sir," came the astonishing reply when I asked our driver the fare. "Just helping out in a bit of a bad time," and, lifting his hat, he whirled away with his car.

II

In the days that were to follow, I was to see the quiet silent strength of England in scores of ways. No one grumbled at the tie-up of railroads, trade transportation, the absence of newspapers, the rapidly declining food-stuffs. There was no fuss. Yet the country was divided into two great opposing camps and on the verge of what Lord Grey over the wireless described as "the greatest crisis since Cromwell's time." We saw hundreds of the strikers calmly working at their little allotments; many were playing tennis and football on the heaths; both sides played cricket together. I saw a train conductor (a striker) and a chimney sweep, with a strong conservative, sitting on the green, smoking their pipes, and talking the strike over as calmly as if they were discussing the weather.

The miners at Durham, which was one of the really bad districts, gave an open-air performance of *Henry VIII* when things were at their worst, and the Northumberland colliers retaliated by giving *Othello*. I talked with butcher, baker, electrician, and railway men. All were marvellous. Whichever their side, there was always good temper and above all a calm dignity.

III

Hooligans and Bolshies they have always with them in England, like most places now, and so I saw a window-smashing. But directly it was over, a wag wrote on the paper-filling of the smashed window:

"Paneless Extraction."

The mob burst into laughter. If there were 4,000,-000 men on strike, there were 6,000,000 volunteers.

London over night equipped 50,000 special con-
stables. You bought your underground ticket, as
usual, at a station, but from a cheery young curate
with a round white collar. The tube lift was worked
by a young man in plus fours. The lift was called a
"Dug Out" everywhere, and they were labelled war
names: "Pipsqueak," "Better 'Ole," etc. A pirate
bus was marked "Jolly Roger" and had a skull and
bones. A Cambridge professor, with monocle neatly
intact, drove a tube. He told me "Engines are my
life hobby." I told him "My life was my hobby."
But I rode just the same. There were fewer accidents than with the regular workers. Trains were
run to schedule, busses driven by youths in rainbow
blazers, luggage footballed about by flappers. But
everything was marvellously disciplined and organ-
ized.

"May I shake hands?" I heard an appreciative old
lady ask an engine driver-volunteer at Waterloo.
The volunteer fireman poked his head out with an
immediate "You may kiss me, madam." Conviction
that all would carry through came from small things
like these.

A delicious story is told by the station-master at
Euston, of a volunteer engineer who single-handed
ran the heavy Scotch express into Euston ten minutes ahead of time. The station-master went to con-
gratulate him, only to find the volunteer engineer, pale

and trembling, asked for a finger or two of brandy and said he had had quite a bad shock.

"How so?" asked the railroad man.

"This ten-minute advance on schedule," he explained. "No credit to me. I just ran by three stations at which this train is supposed to stop."

"Why didn't you stop?" he was asked.

"That's the shock," he explained. "It was only ten minutes ago I found out how to stop this damned thing."

IV

The second day of the strike newspapers practically ceased, and everybody was dependent on the wireless. The wireless in the home of a friend where we were stopping had been whining miserably all winter. But once wireless was threatened by the strikers, this true Britisher machine got its back to the wall, and on picking up the head phones, I found it marvellously clear. Through it we heard all Parliament proceedings and most excellent talks from both sides and those commenters Sir Oliver Lodge, Gilbert Murray, Bernard Shaw, etc.

Lloyd George's effusions were emotional, but hardly convincing. Mr. Baldwin's assurances were admirable, just to both sides, poised, and truly excellent. Ramsay MacDonald was kindly. Lord Grey was charged with that clear, detached, compelling urge

for fair play to both sides. The King was fatherly
and conciliatory, and the Archbishop of Canterbury
very antiquated, with a strong inference that the
God of the Church of England liked order because
he was a well-connected old gentleman who didn't
mind his son taking up carpentering as a hobby, but
believed in working men being kept in their places.
I was interested in discovering that the Church had
little hold. It was the traditional respect for law
that held England. One rector expressed himself
gravely concerned for the nation because, while waiting for the Labor delegation, Mr. Baldwin was not
on his knees praying for England to be spared a revolution.

Mr. Baldwin was found, alas, in the Lion House at
the Zoo.

"Business as usual" was England's motto. Though
I am well aware of the hardships, the financial set-
backs, the aftermath of added taxes, still never have
I known merry England more merry.

V

No transport ran, so every one walked to work.
There was one brigade with every old man between
85 and 92, who walked into London (once). There
were 21 of them who did the marathon. They called
themselves "The Sprinters." Then, a band of old
ladies retaliated. But they only walked half-way into

the town, because people en masse followed them.
They called themselves "The Splinters."

But, here was a sight to go down only with my
going. When no traffic was available, old Lord Roch-
dale, on the hill out at Highgate, bethought himself
of a way. I was walking up the hill when suddenly
I was swept back into the last century. For out of
the open gates of his place where Bacon passed away
came four beautiful "flea-bitten" gray horses, a pos-
tillion and outrider in scarlet and white buckskin
and cockaded gray beaver hats, drawing an old prim-
rose-colored great coach, panelled in black with the
arms of "a peer of the realm." Milord, still fine in
feature, still splendidly irrelevant to the anachronism
of a strike, beckoned any one on to the coach who
wanted to get down-town to work. He took in 20,
and plied all day, while most of the day I was standing at the foot of the hill staring at this miracle of
the continuity of an England of long ago.

VI

The printers went on strike the second day, and
there were almost no papers. But *The Times* got out,
with the help of volunteers, a small, folio sheet, and
in it was the time-honored "Personal" or "Agony
Column," as they call it in England. That agonized
"as usual." Much news was omitted, but "Porcu-
pine" kept on beseeching "Goldilocks" to meet him

under Big Ben at 6, and "Carrots" told "Unicorn" to speak up to her father or she was off to Africa.

Some will recall when, in 1917, the Germans were threatening the Channel Ports and the English were breathless for news, *The Daily Mail* calmly announced that its correspondent (on whom most of London depended) had gone home from the front to his grandmother's funeral in Kent, and so no report was forthcoming! So, when things were at their darkest in this strike, an old General from Dorset published a letter in *The Times* stating that there were not 297 varieties of the beetle in England, as erroneously stated, but 298. He was calm, but perfectly determined that the beetle should get fair play.

Also, at the crisis, the King decided that the insignia of the new order of Knights Bachelor would bear the motto "Eques Auratus," and that spurs with rowels would be fixed horizontally and not vertically.

VII

In one of the darkest moments of the strike it was decided and announced that the Duchess of York's baby would be christened Alexandra for the late Queen, Mary for the present Queen, and Elizabeth for the Duchess.

Once, going up a village street, I saw a passionate mob assembled outside the paper vendor's office. I

heard those low, terribly emotional cries which recalled the first days in Paris of 1914 when the English were threatened, as much by the uncontrolled
mob as by the Germans. The mob was talking vo-
ciferously, and its whole attitude seemed threatening.
I dreaded the result here of a people like the English,
once roused. With my heart in my eyes, I waited
until the roaring crowd disappeared, and then crept
to the window expecting to read that Saklatvala had
captured the House of Parliament. What I read
was that Jack Hobbs had scored 105 runs for Surrey
against the Australians and wasn't out yet.

The second day of the strike the whole "stop"
column in the newspaper was taken up with racing
and the return of the Prince of Wales.

VIII

But what crystallized for me the spirit of England
in this strike was this. In the house where we were
stopping was Laurel, a maid of all work, Laurel whom
our hostess said she kept merely for self-discipline,
and because no one else would have her. Laurel, with
feet like violin cases and legs like the marble Arch,
rushed in one day with: "The Revolution has come."
And then came from her the deep soul cry: "At last
Ernie will be able to play his drum!"

Ernie was her small brother, who was drummer for
the Boy Scouts. He had never been able to have a

real thorough opportunity with his drum. Now Ernie would be able to let go. God help his hearers, I thought, if his muscles were like Laurel's.

There was a nurse, Nannie, in this household. The first morning of the strike I saw Nannie about to dash out into the storm of cold, clinging rain. Her black umbrella was rampant, her voluminous petticoats, her brown hair, all swept out, grim, determined. Nannie was as terrible as an army with banners.

"Nannie," cried her hostess, "why are you dashing out into the storm and strike? There is plenty of food in the house. We mustn't hoard."

"Food," Nannie replied through her clinched new teeth. "Food for 'umans, but none for little Dick in this strike."

Little Dick, or Richard the First, was the canary. When Nannie returned she was soaked and croaking with chill, but she had secured 3 boxes bird seed; 1 box of fish bones, in case a bird doesn't sing enough; 1 box mixed peppers, in case he sings too much; 1 box dried dandelions, in case dandelions go on strike, and a new kind of bird-nail scissors, also "in case." After all the boxes were stored away in a cupboard, and the cupboard locked and the key on a string round Nannie's neck, it only remained to deliver her full feelings on the subject of the miners. But when I explained that miners love canaries, that

they were their safety warners in gaseous mine-pock-
ets, then Nannie's ear-splitting maledictions ceased
and she got out her knitting.

"Well," she said, "I dare say, perhaps, if they
loves canaries they can't be so bad."

CHAPTER FIFTEEN

SOCIAL WHIRLERS

A department we have not in our American newspapers, necessarily, is The Court Circular,—a fact to be regretted, in a sense, because of its fascinating news.

CHAPTER FIFTEEN
SOCIAL WHIRLERS

I

THE daily "Court Circular" was my first excursion into the reading matter of the three newspapers, and I became more fascinated as, daily, I read of the movements of the members of the Royal Family. To think of the Royalties as living lives of luxurious idleness is certainly a delusion, and I wondered at the state of their nerves and digestive processes. The King and Queen were incessantly travelling from London to the Highlands and scores of places in between, opening this Home or Hospital, dedicating a Cathedral, reviewing the Grand Fleet, witnessing a tennis tournament, going to the races, both horse and yacht, giving Garden Parties, receiving this dignitary and that delegation, holding investitures—never a day of rest. While as for the popular Prince of Wales, only the fact that he is thirty and insists upon his daily exercise could keep him fit to keep five or six engagements a day, with a dinner and a ball in the evening. The Duke and Duchess were smiling upon elsewhere throngs: the Duke of Connaught was in Wales and everywhere else: the Princess Marie Louise was busy opening the hospitals that the King and Queen couldn't get to. Everybody was busy.

II

But I really became thrilled with following the social doings of the lesser knighted folk who figure in the middle of the "Court Circular." There was Lady Ernestine Burghclerc and Bucclench, for example. Her Ladyship attracted me first by her plentiful names, and then I became breathlessly interested in her trips out of London. In five weeks she "entrained" on four trips, and each time she "left Claridge's," which I thought was so considerate of her, so that others could enjoy the hotel while she was absent. On one trip she went to Paris, and I could not help following her to the French capital, wondering about the havoc that the shop girls along the Rue de la Paix must have wrought with Her Ladyship's name when she wanted a purchase sent to her hotel. The greatest social feat of Lady Ernestine—if I may be so bold to call her that—occurred, however, when she gave "a tea at Claridge's (in London) at four this afternoon" and also "a garden party at her beautiful Highland estate at three this afternoon." I thought this was a busy afternoon for Her Ladyship until I looked up the railroad time-table and found that her "Highland estate" was situated five hours by train from London. Then my admiration for Lady Ernestine's dexterity grew. I thought of two Ladyships: of a private aeroplane, and my impatience was

keen to see the next morning's *Times* to see how Her
Ladyship had survived her double function. She apparently did, because the account was very careful
to show how well Her Ladyship looked in "a most
becoming gown." But this was at the tea, and complete silence reigned over the garden party five hours
away.

III

I now became transfixed in interest over The Honorable Mrs. Blundell-Bendir Fetherstonhaugh who,
according to "The Court and Personal" never seemed
to dine at home. It evidently wore on the honorable
lady after three weeks, for then she "repaired to
Deuville," and I couldn't help feeling that the social
chronicler had chosen exactly the right word. Lady
Clodagh and Hawke Price fascinated me, too; she
was also a very busy lady. But when a musical evening was given at her house at which Mr. Wellbe-
loved sang and Miss Pretyman Scrachemwell played
the violin, I was simply entranced. I could not help
wondering how the music fitted the names.

IV

The distinguished couple whose social movements
interested me the most were Mr. and Mrs. Hwfa
Kenwood of Nunburnholme House. This active social gentleman's name held me like a vice, and I wondered what the footmen, the best of whom are mas-

ters in the pronunciation of names, did when they announced the advent of this couple. Then I found out that they were always wary. It was invariably "Mr. and Mrs. Kenwood" who entered the drawing-room. I tried my best to run down the pronunciation of Mr. Kenwood's Christian name, because I suspected that you pronounced the H, whistled the w and played the fa on the piano. Then I met a friend of his, and I sprung the trap.

"Nice chap, Kenwood, isn't he?" I suggested.

"Yes, quite all right," was the answer.

"What is his first name?" I asked.

"Ah, Kenwood's? Oh, I think it's H, isn't it?" he asked of another in the group.

"Quite right," was the answer. And no one "saw."

Then I wondered what his intimates called him. But calling one by his Christian name "isn't done" in England, as a rule, and so perhaps by that door they escape in this case.

I even tried to ascertain how Mrs. Kenwood addressed him, only to find that she, too, was wary, and steadily referred to "my husband."

I remembered now that only one other name bothered me quite so much as did the front handle of Mr. Kenwood's name. That was the name of the gentleman in the past who was responsible, according to Ambrose, for bringing the waltz-form into the people's realm of music. His name was Krch.

CHAPTER SIXTEEN

HIS MAJESTY AND HER MAJESTY

Americans sometimes think that independence is a virtue peculiar to America and that it suddenly sprang into life in the world on the Fourth of July, 1776. This incident would seem to show, however, that a rich leaven of independence exists elsewhere.

CHAPTER SIXTEEN
HIS MAJESTY AND HER MAJESTY

I

WHEN the present King George of England married he built York Cottage—comparatively a moderate-sized house—which he wanted as a quiet, care-free home. He centred here his family life, as he and Queen Mary do to-day, and here he takes his holidays from State duties. He loves to indulge here his particular recreation: shooting, since he is truly a skilful shot.

Since the Great War the King has turned all his available Norfolk land into farming, save some certain rough stubble and bracken acres which are kept for his shooting. And these happen to form a sort of a horseshoe for the sportsman-king. These acres frame some intervening pasture-land, so that whenever the royal party goes hunting, it must make a long detour to get round this particular piece of land. Furthermore, the King can shoot no pheasants which fly over this land, as he has no shooting rights over it. The birds seem to have divined this, with the result that they have adopted it as a sanctuary, and there are more pheasants to the square foot in this piece of land than in the whole of the King's acreage.

II

It was perfectly natural, therefore, that His Majesty conceived the idea of purchasing this land, and when a King wants anything he generally gets it. So he ordered his agent to ascertain the owner, and purchase the land, so as to square off his acreage and make his shooting more successful. To ascertain the owner was, of course, very simple: the record had simply to be looked up. Likewise to make an offer, and naturally the King's agent simply waited to have his royal master's offer accepted.

But it was precisely at that point that a cog in the simple machinery appeared. The acceptance did not come. Instead there came a note saying "Certainly not. Three acres and a cow are all any one should have." And there was a decisive tone in the answer that left nothing to be desired in its conclusiveness.

III

The King's agent was amazed. The King was not: he was intensely interested and amused. "Who is this owner?" he asked.

Then the curtains in the negotiations parted, and there was revealed a wonderful old lady of the real Norfolk type. She was the descendant of one of the oldest Norfolk families, and as George was only a

Windsor and a distinct newcomer (of only fifty years)
in the parish, he must be kept in his place.

That was thirty years ago. But the matter of the
land stands exactly where it stood then. The land
of the old lady of Norfolk is not for sale, the shooting
rights cannot be had, and the King had been told that
no man can set foot on this land without those due
rights.

So for thirty years York Cottage and the little red-
brown home of the old lady have faced each other.
For thirty years the Royal Shooting Parties have
made their detour and avoided her land full of birds.
For thirty years the King has sighed and sighed again,
while the old lady has shaken her pretty cap until
she is quite ready to slip into the Nursery Rhyme
which children of the future will one day be lisping
about her:

> "Come, come," said he quite royally,
>   "Do let me buy that land!"
> "Nay, nay," said she, "kind Sir, prithee,
>   'Tis not yours to command!"
>   Tra-la-la, la-la!

IV

One goes through a typical Norfolk lane, gorgeously
burnished with the autumn colors, with pheasants
walking tamely across the road, to the old lady's
house. Small, unpretentious, filled with a curious

English hominess in its haphazard roof, it ripples with mosses and ivy and brown curlycue gables. Bright diamond-paned windows smile on the roses pillared below, the cooing pigeons, some late wisps of lavender, and the tennis court where the celebrated parties are a County event.

Beyond these is the kitchen garden, with its cabbages and roses, potatoes and daisies, alternating in the English fashion. Again beyond that, through a loop of privet, lay those famous fields which the King of England wants and wants and keeps on wanting. One stands at the white gate and looks at those fields.

And why does the King want those acres? One looks to the far distance. Just between the glimmer of the Norfolk Broads—those shining water-ways which are the canals of this County—the skyscape is cut by the towers of York Cottage.

V

It happens that this lady standing guard over her land and permitting no trespass upon the part of the King is as well preserved as she is courageous. She is a plump, ageless little great-grandmother. Her sparkling black eyes are clear as those of a robin. Her muslin cap laughs at one's expression of wonder at her absolute erectness. She walks without any stick, straight as the tall clock in her beautiful hallway. The black rafters of her rooms are mellow with age:

the steaming kettle over the slow peat fire sings of centuries, the sparkling Punch and Judy on the mantel, the jug of blue anchusas in the low window framed with crimson ramblers—everything seems instinct with the lady's happiness. Like herself, the beautiful pieces of old furniture, which a connoisseur would envy, had long since found an angle of repose.

VI

Why had she refused to sell her land to the King of England? It was part of her home, this home of her forefathers, and it had been theirs for generations. They had come here in the old Viking days, before even King George's long lineage had taken root in Norman adventurers. Long centuries stretched on behind her in this home.

The hand that poured tea was crissed and crossed with the deep-rooted inheritances of men who had loved this home. They had built and re-built it, until its every beam was a chapter in their family history. For centuries they had farmed here, and they had gone out from here to pioneer other lands, or to fight for this home as their country called. The old lady's own children, her grandchildren and great-grandchildren had gone forth from this pleasant room to find new homes in earth's far corners, for in this old lady's seed, like Abraham's, the nations of the world have been blessed.

VII

For be it said, not whispered, because she is very proud of the fact, that this wonderful old lady of Norfolk is 102 years old.

When she referred to her recent loss of a daughter only 82 years old, she added, "but then, Mary was always delicate."

And she says this quite simply as she sits serene, deep-thinking, self-poised, inestimably happy. She speaks of England's long century to which she has been eye-witness, from "Little Victoria's coronation" to "that nice young man (who happens to be the present Prince of Wales) who comes down to see me when he is at York Cottage sometimes, for a quiet talk together."

Sometimes she speaks of her love of simple comfort: her belief in its recipe for old age, and the passing of simplicity from present-day life. When she speaks of the latter one sees the snap of her black eye, and you feel its power as did one unfortunately now notorious young man last summer. He lit a cigarette on her tennis lawn when one of her famous parties was in full swing, every detail of which she personally arranges.

"Young man," her crisp voice stated a fact, not a question, "you are smoking a cigarette in my presence and in the presence of other ladies. You have not asked my permission, nor would I have given it. Your own presence is excused, Sir."

VIII

Deeply, affectionately, too, she touches on the village life that has passed beside her window, which looks out on the inevitable Green with its squat-towered Norman church, the duck pond and the play-ground. All of these her own people have helped to pioneer. Out there four generations had given her their laughter, their cricket, their Maypole and their Yuletide, and not less a village feast in these latter years, her great white birthday cake. On that village green she has heard not once, but many times in her century, the drum decide that England expects that every man will do his duty. Lately she heard it call again—first the village lads, then the fathers of those who had fallen. All these had come into her little room, and they had said their quiet, off-hand good-bys. And then their widows and sweethearts had come a bit later and sat here and gained courage to face the empty years.

"Just living life gives courage to face life," she told them all.

And yet it still seemed a curious thing that in this century of woman's so-called emancipation, when millions have sought and sometimes attained careers out of their homes, this wonderful old lady has achieved immortality only because she loved her home (which she has never left for more than three days together) even beyond price. For it came to that—the price—in her last battle with the King of England.

IX

Last year on the verge of confessing himself defeated by the old lady's thirtieth refusal of his agent's offer, King George had a new thought. He had never sought to buy her home, nor did he in any way wish more than the shooting rights of her land. Now it was represented to him that taxes were high. Any living, even of a hundred and two years, was expensive.

"It would be a real kindness," he was urged, "to help the old lady by offering a good price for the shooting rights of that land she would not sell. Why not offer her a good lease for all her land?"

So again came autumn, again the brilliant burnish of the bracken, again the whirring rainbows of the pheasants' wings, again came the interruption of the Royal Shooting Party by the detour round her pastures; and again came the King's agent knocking at the door.

X

And this time the royal offer was so kindly bounteous it left her gasping. "Just to lease those fields."

"I must see," said the old lady as she stood to her last battle, "I must see."

So she took up her black umbrella, and went out and walked about those fields that had been the fields of her fathers, and fathers' fathers. They had been handed down to her in sacred trust as part of the little home which in itself had been a nucleus for village life in the centuries.

One could just see the little straight-backed figure, with its old-fashioned bobbing walk, rounding up those pastures the day of her decision. One could follow her old mind thinking of the pheasants and their ancient sanctuary in the little spinney at the bottom of the pastures; of the men and women who had come back to her from the four corners of the world, and sat in this home and looked out on those pastures and said: "Wherever we are we know they are here like you, waiting for us to come home to."

On that day of the agent's visit, while she went bobbing about her fields with her black umbrella, she must have put the things to one side of her credits, to the other side she must have debited the worry of the encroaching years, heavily increased taxes, many little comforts to be foregone. But what were these over against the saying of those: "Wherever we are we know they are here like you, waiting for us to come to"?

One can see her grip that black umbrella and come

back and give the royal agent her quiet "No. My compliments to His Majesty. I cannot sell nor let my land."

XI

Then there came a pretty sequel. The old lady's final answer was given to the King. "She has refused to let even the shooting rights of her pastures. She says it is the land of her fathers and she would keep it intact with her home," he repeated. A quiet sparkle lit his eye. Then he burst into the ringing laugh of one who after thirty years of battle has fought a good fight and lost—with admiration for his victor.

"Well done," he cried. "Well done. If a home and land are worth all that I must go down and see them."

So it came about that on her 102d birthday, while the old lady of Norfolk sat in her fragrant room with her huge cake before her, crowned with its candles, surrounded with gifts, letters, and telegrams from all over the world, there was a lull, as she waited for her guests to come crowding in.

"A very special admirer is at the door, ma'am," she was told. "He wants to come in quietly by himself."

And in he came, just a country neighbor in his tweeds, his kindly face shaded with reverence and humor. Thus the rivals of thirty years met over the

old lady's 102d birthday cake. He did not wish her
to know the King of England was calling. While the
old lady recognized the well-known face of many
years, she was too royal herself at heart to betray
her King's quiet pleasure. So with only the faintest
twinkle between these legended rivals she accepted
all his kindest birthday wishes with her curtsey. And
then she lit one early candle on her mountainous
cake, and asked "Will you make a wish?"

XII

Now a birthday wish, of course, must be a secret
one or it won't come true. Certainly the King did
not tell his. But sitting in this quiet room, so at one
with its memories of the old lady herself smiling upon
one, one likes to guess that when, on her 102d birthday, these two landowners met eye to eye, the silent
wish of George by the Grace of God, King of England and Ireland, Defender of the Faith, etc., must
have been that wish of which the old lady of Norfolk
had taught him the value:

"Defenders of the faith in our homes—long may
they reign."

CHAPTER SEVENTEEN

LONDON'S LADS AND LASSIES

One would never accuse the English of it. But there it was, in cold print, day by day. I say "cold print." But, after a while, the type itself must have grown warm for the messages which it was asked to carry.

CHAPTER SEVENTEEN
LONDON'S LADS AND LASSIES

I

I DIDN'T get all the picture that my doctor pictured. By the time the strike was over, the may was over. The strawberries were there, and as I had heard about Devonshire cream I went to the Devonshire coast. There I found both the cream and the strawberries, and they found me so promptly that on the second day between spasms of pain I heartily agreed with the dietitian that strawberries were only food for pigs!

I had been told by The Man of Medicine to stroll over the Devonshire moors, and lie on the Tintangel cliffs where Isolde is supposed to have sung to Tristan the most glorious love song ever written. I don't doubt that this is possible, and profitable. But one mustn't, in that case, subscribe to the three leading London newspapers. Important international news was flying around, and I wanted to keep up with it. Parliament was in session. The House of Lords "sat" and "rose," and, so far as I could see, this distinguished House did this every day and nothing else. But it takes a London chronicler quite a time to tell this. Sports were very active. So were Egyptian and India affairs.

French affairs were particularly so. The result was that when I was through with these papers I could do nothing for the balance of the day because there was no balance left.

II

Of course, I might have omitted reading the advertisements. But how could I help it? There it was—right on the first page the very first day when I meant to find a Devonshire moor:

FRED: Why do you let me starve?
MOST BEAUTIFUL.

Now I ask you how can any one pass an advertisement like that without at least giving it a thought? I did. How was "Fred" starving "Most Beautiful"? Emotionally, economically, mentally? And *why* was "Fred" starving "Most Beautiful"? Why would any man want to starve a "most beautiful" woman? You couldn't pass an advertisement like that, no matter how the news calls.

Of course, the next day I looked for Fred's apology, or at least explanation. None. Nor the next day. But "Most Beautiful" came again!

FRED: No answer. Why do you let my soul yearn? Life has all but stopped. I wait, and yearn.
MOST BEAUTIFUL.

Then the starving was a soulful yearn. That much was settled. But why didn't "Fred" answer? Surely to have a "most beautiful" woman's life all but stop *was* a responsibility for any man to carry. Why let her "wait and yearn"?

For days it was I who feverishly waited and yearned. Then, at last, "Fred" awoke to his responsibility:

MOST BEAUTIFUL: Your beauty is an echo of the hymn sung at the break of day by Seraphim.

FRED.

Just like that. But that was all. Would it satisfy "Most Beautiful"? I didn't think it would, and it didn't. The very next day this:

FRED: Beautiful thought. It comforted me. But when and where can I see you? So anxious, so lonely.

MOST BEAUTIFUL.

Of course. I knew it. You can't be just a poet alone with a "most beautiful" woman, and let it go at that! You must have the qualities of a "meeter" as well, and recognize there is an earth and on that earth meeting-places for those who are "anxious" and "so lonely." But "Fred" refused to be smoked out, and "Most Beautiful" came again:

FRED: Day by day, I look and look. Every day seems a hundred years.

MOST BEAUTIFUL.

Think of days as long as that! Surely, I thought, "Fred" must capitulate now. But he didn't. Thus he printed:

MOST BEAUTIFUL: I think of you much. Will always do so. But why pursue our friendship with meetings? It can lead nowhere. So why torture ourselves?   FRED.

What would "Most Beautiful" do now, I wondered. She was "thrown down"—politely, yet unmistakably thrown. I grew feverish with excitement, and of course that led straight to hot water and bicarbonate of soda!

III

Then, to make matters worse, "Fred" and "Most Beautiful" were not the only ones in distress. In between, "Doreen" and her "Dear Boy" began to clamor for each other. This time it was the male pursuing the female. Evidently "Doreen" had been neglectful:

DOREEN: Feel frightfully neglected and alone. Write and give me hope and appoint meeting-place soon. I hunger to look into that face which means so much to me.
DEAR BOY.

But "Dear Boy" didn't come through with an advertisement. But evidently he did with a letter, for this was next:

DEAR BOY: Be cautious. Letter seen by some one else. I warn you.

DOREEN.

"Dear Boy" now seems to have been cautious for three days. But even Caution will wear out in that time. So, on the fourth day, he pined:

DOREEN: Shall not write again, but will you not see me? There is no one else in life but you. I want you.

DEAR BOY.

But, apparently, "Doreen" didn't want her "Dear Boy," and the fact that there was no one else in his life did not seem to alter the fact that there *was* some one else in her life. So silence brooded.

Not over "Sweet Lavender," however. She began in the most frisky manner, and fairly bubbled over her "Jimmy."

She began:

JIMMY: Where are you, and why do I not hear? Do you know you are everything to me, circumstances notwithstanding? Your course of action is clear. Come to me.

SWEET LAVENDER.

Now "Jimmy" had something of the Scotch in him. Six pence a word, thought he, and so laconically, he answered:

SWEET LAVENDER: Where?

JIMMY.

Back came "Sweet Lavender" the next day:

Jimmy: Wherever you say. But somewhere where we won't be seen.　　　　　Sweet Lavender.

Whatever possessed "Jimmy" I can't imagine, for he answered:

Sweet Lavender: Piccadilly Club 1 Tuesday.
　　　　　　　　　　　　　　　　　　　Jimmy.

Of course, the sequel might have been known:

Jimmy: Are you purposely cruel? Went to Club which is only for men. Paced up and down front until attracted attention. I want you so much. Make suitable appointment.　　　　　Sweet Lavender.

But no "come back" came from Jimmy.

IV

The English spring now got thoroughly into the blood of these unhappy English lads and lassies, and all broke out together. Not only they, but "Derry Dear" and "Theda" started up. So did "Phil" and "Kit." "Doreen" became kindlier to her "Dear Boy." "Fred" and "Most Beautiful" simply couldn't live apart long enough to put their advertisements in the paper, "Sweet Lavender" and "Jimmy" were in daily activity, and my head began to twirl, and it wasn't long before I had them all mixed up, and it took me hours to straighten them out.

But when "Columbine" and "Harqueline" began, and "Alabaster" started with "Mimosa," and "Tim" and "Dora" got going, I began to feel that all London seemed to be getting affected by the springtime. The pace was too fast for me, particularly when "Angel Cake" and "Nectarine" started up:

ANGEL CAKE: A kiss as gentle as the dew. Sunlight to unfold thy beauty. Waves on a broken shore to speak the discord in my thoughts.

NECTARINE.

That certainly should elicit something for "Nectarine." And it did—it certainly did. It should have, for that matter:

NECTARINE: Your wonderful words brought forth all my longings and I went to sleep thinking of you and dreamed of you all night—dreams as gentle as the pimpernel, elusive, exclusive.

ANGEL CAKE.

Of course, I rushed to the dictionary to find out what kind of dreams "pimpernel" dreams were. I found out, of course. Evidently bad weather was approaching, as all the genus pimpernel close when the skies darken. But no! For next day I read:

ANGEL CAKE: Keep our promise to one another, and no skies will darken our wonderful love. We must wait and

long, wait and long until the world is kind again to us. I
am your mouse, your watchdog, your eagle, your Bird of
Paradise.

NECTARINE.

I began to try and figure out which was which.
Was "Nectarine" the male, or was it "Angel Cake"?
When the very next day came this:

NECTARINE: My life is one long imprisonment without
you. I simply cannot go along alone. Every day is the
longest day of the year. I crave, I yearn, I long. No peace
can I find. Darling, my darling! do not hesitate.

ANGEL CAKE.

Now, I thought, Nectarine will certainly do something. But what did he or she do? I still wonder, for
now my day was the longest of the year, for I could
not fathom this cryptic reply:

ANGEL CAKE: Kumble. Exumble. Numble. Mumble.
Wumble. Prumble. Three Sumbles make a Bumble.

NECTARINE.

Perhaps they do.
But I gave up!

CHAPTER EIGHTEEN
WILLIAM SHAKESPEARE
ROAD SWEEP

We were fortunate enough to run across an impression in Stratford-on-Avon which has escaped the American tourists who have gone there, and which I think is worthy of being put down here—two vignettes of the town and folk of Stratford which made a very strong appeal to The Lady and me.

CHAPTER EIGHTEEN

WILLIAM SHAKESPEARE

ROAD SWEEP

I

IT was that soft dusk which shrouds Stratford-on-Avon in a warm after-sunlight that threw a rich glow over the South border of Susanna Hall's garden, indescribably gay with lupine and early holly-hock and the fine old-fashioned Tudor posies. We had just been inside the house, and were still in the 1610 picture of a rather stout well-shaped man of fifty sitting before the big fireplace in the hall, reading to his daughter about "We are such stuff as dreams are made of," and hoping all would go well for Burbage at the Globe.

We had been fancying the times when Susanna and her father had been walking along the same path in the garden, and had just clicked the gate shut and turned for a last look at the gay borders in the garden when there smote upon our ears:

"'Ave you seen Shaxpeare about?"

We looked at each other and blinked. We looked down the road whence an old man, calling to another, gray and hearty and wearing a white smock, had asked the question which had startled us. They were road-sweepers pushing their long-handled refuse-pans.

"Will you h'ask Shaxpeare to come by?" the man again called to the other. Again our ears flapped, and we looked at each other. Our hands were still on the garden-gate.

Then we heard the second sweep call: "Will, O Will, come by."

II

Into view came a third sweep with the uniform smock, and he joined his two fellows. As he stood talking to them, he swept off his high-steeple crowned straw hat, and there stood before us in the life the head and face of the Shakespeare of the First Folio. We stared at the resemblance. The fine forehead, the high and wide, pronounced circling eyebrows, the closely set intuitive eyes, and the mouth kindly and humorous, all were there revealed to our astonished gaze.

It was too much. We could not let him go. So we approached him.

Yes, his name was William Shakespeare, a road-sweeper for some twenty years, taken for granted by the home folk, overlooked by the thousands of tourists who swirl and eddy through the town.

Farm laborer by previous profession; now road-sweeper.

From Shottery? "Yes," was the simple, sincere answer. "Where all Shakespeares was come by first in these parts. The writer's grandfather was brother to my ancestor. His folk moved over here," as he stood twirling his hat and resting on the handle of his pan.

"And you were named for the great William?" we asked.

A hurt look came into the fine eyes, and then with perfect sincerity: "Oh, no. For my father."

Thus did he sweep aside any clinging to the man of world fame, giving a perfectly true example of how incidental, how wonderfully and completely incidental, all outside glory is to the single stem of English life as one learns it in Warwickshire.

"William," he continued, "is always the first boy's name with us. Father and son."

There was the story of Stratford. Who dies if England lives? And can England ever die when such as this William Shakespeare works at his daily sweeping, perfectly calm, extraordinarily at peace. There stood the symbol of an affectionate allegiance to his own. No gilding the small village tanner-father with the glamor of the world ancestor. It was marvellous how one felt the power of England in the quiet dignity, the simplicity, and the contentment of this man Shakespeare.

III

No, no photographer had ever taken his picture.
No correspondent had ever written about him. No,
he never spoke to tourists unless they asked him the
way. He had never been in the birthplace. Nor New
Place. He had heard that the hollyhocks were particularly fine at Susanna Hall's, and there was the
flicker of a smile at the mention of the flowers.

No, he had never read any of Shakespeare's works.
He had begun to work at eleven; had never had time
to learn to read or write. Seventy-four now. "Too
late now to learn," and again that smile of contentment.

No, he didn't want anything; just to keep on with
his job of road-sweeping.

"Keeping the place tidy," to "watch the folk pass
by," and "think on them when I am at home evenings."

No, he had never been in the church where his great
ancestor lay grandly with the world coming to his
bier.

Simply, but so full of power he said: "You see it is
not my parish. I am a Shottery man. My church is
there. My wife, too, lies there."

More to him, far more, than that the world-figure in
his ancestor should lie in the Stratford parish.

He spoke of his sons and grandsons. "They have

done well." Carpenters were they; printers, stained-glass workers. No, no authors, he said. No stressing of antecedal connections or heritage to take them away from the work for which they were fitted: no artificial leaning on name or reputation.

The birds he knew, and could bring them to him. The trees he loved and patted their bark.

IV

Americans? No, he knew none. He had only spoken to one once. "Very kindly," was his comment of the Americans.

So we left him in the glow of the setting sun: power-ful in the night of his absolute simplicity, passed by unknowingly each year by thousands of tourists from every part of the world: William Shakespeare: road-sweep!

V

When New Place, Shakespeare's residence, was torn down by the Canon living there, a vast amount of rubbish remained behind. In the restoration, a la-borer, Joseph Smith, Junior, by name, found a black-ened brooch. Smith was a cooper by trade, but a poor craftsman. He wandered from job to job. That eve-ning one of his ten children began to cry, and to quiet it he gave the child the pin brooch he had found in the Shakespeare rubbish. The child played with it, it

was passed to the other children, who, in turn, shined
it up, and revealed a gold brooch set with small
brilliants, three of which were missing. On the reverse side was plainly cut the name: W Shakespeare.

Smith was an unlettered man, and knew nothing of
Shakespeare as a writer. One day he took the brooch
from one of his children, and so that the child could
not find it again he pinned it inside his vest. Soon,
thereafter, the town of Stratford presented *Merry
Wives of Windsor* as a play. Smith saw it and liked
"Falstaff." It was the kind of a character he could
understand. Then the town gave *Midsummer Night's
Dream*, and he saw that. Smith began to like what
he saw, and thought he would like to read one of
Shakespeare's plays. Painfully and laboriously he
taught himself to read. He was fifty-two years of age,
and the process was hard. After that he was always
found in some part of a field or under some hedge
with a book by Shakespeare, spelling out the words.
The lines, "All the world's a stage," became a favorite
with him, and when he did work he was always re-
citing the words of his favorite passage. One day he
found the pin stuck in his vest, and it began to have
a new value to him as belonging to the man whose
lines had fascinated him. But his reading lost work
for him, and his wife sold the pin, in desperate want for
her children. Smith was furious when he found this
out, and worked and saved until he had money enough

to buy the pin back. The Clerk of the Parish arrested Smith for not supporting his family, and buying an extravagance like a pin, and he was sent to the workhouse.

VI

Some one had seen the pin when Smith's wife had sold it, and the town officials of Stratford now set out to buy the pin, which they traced back and found had been the actual property of Shakespeare. But Smith would not part with the pin. The town officials refused to shelter him in its workhouse unless he sold the pin. From parish poorhouse to parish poorhouse he went. Finally he could find shelter nowhere, and he lived under the hedges and ditches. But he would not part with the pin or his dirty copy of Shakespeare plays. He deserted his wife and children. Meanwhile the authenticity of the brooch had been established beyond a doubt; moreover, it was found that, for some unknown reason, it had been particularly valued by Shakespeare and that he carried it wherever he went.

A magistrate explained to Smith that he could rescue his wife and family with the money he could secure from the town of Stratford for the brooch.

"No," he answered, "I will not sell it. I gave all my younger manhood days to working for my wife and children, and I got no other return than a scold for a wife and a lot of ungrateful children who did me the only good turn they ever did when they sucked off the grime from this brooch. That brooch brought me to the man who once owned it, and through him I learned to read and to know of a new world of books and people. I learned to laugh and to live, and I am not going to sell this brooch."

VII

Finally his health failed, and he was taken to the Stratford workhouse to pass away. Every day he would sit up in bed, read Shakespeare's plays, laugh, and all the while he would clean and shine his brooch.

Then he passed away, with the brooch in his hand. The town bought the precious relic, one of the few personal possessions in existence to-day of Shakespeare known to be genuine, and the proceeds were spent for his wife and children.

To-day when the town-folk of Stratford tell the story of the Shakespeare brooch, they gravely shake their heads and say, with great emphasis: "It was the undoing of Smith."

But was it his undoing?

I doubt if the original owner of the brooch would have thought so!

VIII

I venture to add to these two little Stratford vignettes.

There is a queer little comedy going on in the town of Stratford-on-Avon: in the house where Marie Corelli lived. A caller there has the door opened for him by a sinister old man who, for over thirty years, was the author's butler. To him, Miss Corelli left, in her will, the right to live in the house so long as her lifelong companion, Miss Vyver, lives there. There is also a chauffeur who served the writer half a lifetime, and to him she left her 1908 Daimler car. But the silver angel on the engine-hood she left to the butler, although the chauffeur was to have the use of it on the car during his lifetime.

Hence the comedy—it is a tragedy to those concerned—is that Miss Vyver feels that she does not want to keep up the house, and chooses to sell it. But she cannot eject the butler, and he doesn't want to get out. The butler wants the silver angel on the Daimler, but can't have it until the chauffeur passes away. The chauffeur can't afford to keep the car in repair unless he sells the silver angel, which is the only valuable thing about the automobile, and this he cannot legally do.

So, some one of the three has got to pass away. And that speedily. But neither of the three chooses to do so.

The silver angel really holds the key to the situation. Meanwhile, the angel just waits, and, sometimes, Stratford folk say, it winks!

CHAPTER NINETEEN

PLEASANT TIMES WERE THESE!

I once heard one of these deeply thoughtful young men, just out of Seminary, ask a minister who had grown gray and mellow in the service of his work: "Don't you think, Sir, that Christianity has proved a failure?"

The venerable preacher's answer was very quiet: "I didn't know, my boy, that it had even been tried."

That our ideas of Christianity have materially changed was impressed upon me while we were in England.

CHAPTER NINETEEN
PLEASANT TIMES WERE THESE!

I

WE were in an English country house, and I was studying the guide-book to learn our way for the next day's run.

"Ever see an English guide-book, of the seventeenth century?" asked my host, as he put a book in my hand. "Look it over, and see how travellers were guided in those days."

I read this:

Pass gallows on left and three gibbets on right into York. A small ascent: then pass the gallows to Corkehill. Pass through Hare Street with gallows on left, up a small hill with gibbet on right. At end of road cross brook and pass by gallows: leave acute way to gallows where Southworth malefactors are executed: at 8.5 you pass gallows on left: leave Petersborough and pass gallows on right: then over a stone road past gibbet on left, ascend a hill and pass by gallows: up a steep hill past gallows on left.

It does not require a vivid imagination from these guide-helps to realize that they used gallows and stakes and gibbets rather freely in those days. It didn't take much of a pretext upon which to hang or burn a poor wretch: man or woman. Twenty thousand was the toll in England of witches alone, and all because of a religious mania. And those whom they didn't burn or hang, they had a gentle way of torturing. That was before and during the reign of James I. But he had troubles of his own. He was not a beauty, was James, with his hideous face, his misshapen form, and his distorted mind, as those who have read of this fated monarch know. It was James who put up a great many of the gallows and public stakes, and it was not to be wondered at that Queen Elizabeth had her hands full to find him a wife. James was unwilling, and the girls were shy—naturally. It was Anne, Princess of Denmark, who at last said she would be James's Queen, due to the fact that she was fifteen. But James wouldn't go to Denmark: was superstitious of travel, and after a flattering painting was made of his Queen-to-be, he agreed to marry her sight unseen. So, by proxy, they were married. Then did James send a fleet of his ships to Denmark to bring his Queen to him, but a storm hit the fleet, sunk the ships, and drowned nearly the entire crew and officers. "Send another," calmly ordered the King, and forthwith another fleet was despatched, and that was likewise sunk almost in its entirety. "Witches," said the King. "Nonsense," said little Anne, "let me try. I'll take a lot of our ships." But no sooner had she put her royal feet on one of the ships when a storm broke, carried the ships away from England instead of to it, and finally washed the little Queen on the coast of Denmark. "It's all because I'm a Catholic and she a Protestant," explained the King. "To hell with the Fates. I'll go and fetch her." This time he got to her, and stayed in Denmark until the ice went out. But to get even with the Fates which had sought to keep him from his wife, he got busier than ever when he returned to England, and hung, burned, and tortured every one who showed the slightest trend toward witchery.

Pleasant times those!

III

He believed, did James, that the witches and wizards and the Devil had conspired to prevent his marriage and then his acquirement of his bride. He believed to the last syllable an account that was given by one misguided "Elder" on the scaffold how a meeting was held the previous Halloween night in a little kirk on the Scottish coast. Two hundred witches had gathered at the instance of the Devil. A graphic account of this amazing figment of the imagination is given in Gemmill's *Witch Trials*.

The night was wild and stormy, we are told by this chronicler, but this only increased the fiendish pleasure of the worshippers. Some came by sea, riding in sieves, others flew through the air on broomsticks, some rode on goats, some on swine, some on dogs, and some on black cats. Time and distance were annihilated.

The Devil was there in the form of a he-goat. His nose was like an eagle's beak, his body hard as iron, his eyes like fire-balls, his voice like the east wind, his hands and legs were covered with long hair, scorpion thongs were fastened to his belt. In one hand he held a black image for the witches to kiss, in the other he held a flaming torch. When the witches arrived the kirk was dark, but each witch carried in her hand a candle which burned with a blue flame. All saluted the Devil, who stood in front of the kirk, then they circled 'round and 'round, in a wild sensuous dance, led by Geillis Duncan, who played a reel upon a jews-harp. All were naked and danced back to back. Sometimes the Devil played on a bagpipe and sometimes on a flute. If the dancers lagged, he lashed their bare bodies with his scorpion whips, and the burning feet of the dancers moved so swiftly about the kirk that the grass was withered, and until this day nothing will grow thereon.

When the dance had finished, the teller of the yarn told how he blew his fiery breath into the keyhole and the kirk became a blaze of light. All entered through cracks in the door and beheld the Devil sitting in the pulpit, in the form of a he-goat, and clothed in a black gown and hat.

When all were inside, the roll was called and each

wizard and witch arose and told what he or she had
done since they last met. Some had killed the neighbors' cattle, or sheep, or swine. Others had inflicted
death, or rheumatism, or gout. Some destroyed crops,
withered trees and fruit. Some had driven needles
through the brains of little children. The greater
the misery inflicted the happier was Satan, who alter-
nately smiled and frowned as he listened to the re-
ports. One old witch reported that she had done nothing since last they met. The Devil leaped upon her
and beat her.

IV

When the roll was finished, new members were received. A solemn oath was administered by the
Devil, wherein each one swore to deny God, to curse,
blaspheme, and provoke Him and His disciples, to
worship Satan and do his commandments, to lay
waste the fruits of the earth, to send disease and
death into cattle, swine, and horses, to blight corn,
and the harvest, to engender hate, stir up wrath, and
do evil everywhere, to avenge the Devil against all
his enemies, by afflicting them with pain, loathsome
disease, and famine, to make desolate the fields and
the heart of man, to ravish the graves of the dead,
and haunt the homes of the living.

When this ceremony ended, all kissed the Devil on
his back, and received a mark in the flesh burned by
a red-hot iron.

At last came the banquet, and a merry feast it was. Unbaptized children were served. They had been boiled in a red hot caldron until the flesh became ointment. Some of the bodies had been taken from new-made graves. Some had recently been strangled. Some were still-born. While the kettle boiled, all danced 'round and 'round it.

Into the steaming kettle were thrown noses, fingers, and toes that had been gathered from rifled graves, and the entrails of children and every foul and venomous beast and serpent. The meal was served without salt and flavor, and all who ate were as hungry as before.

Finally the Devil stamped his hoofs upon the floor and all was dark. The church was empty. The witches had vanished as they had come.

It is hard to conceive that any man could believe such a yarn. But James did, and on the strength of it he multiplied his killings. Evidently Shakespeare did not draw upon his imagination in the witches' scene in *Macbeth*. It was all in the literature of his day: in the minds of the people: in their daily lives. It is upon all these horrible fantasies of disordered minds that our present Halloween is based.

V

It is hard for us to grasp in these days what the people of those days actually believed: that animals were possessed of the devil and that scores of actual court-trials of animals occurred in the fifteenth and sixteenth centuries. Wild animals were tried by the church and its courts: domestic animals by the civic courts. You have only to read the history of that period if the credulity is strained. Dogs were regularly tried in the Roman courts. Roosters that laid enormous eggs and black cats were favorite defendants. A rooster with a propensity for laying eggs was tried in Basle in 1774 and, condemned, the cock and his egg burned at the public stake. Regular summonses were issued for the animals to appear in court, and if after three summonses they did not appear, they were tried without the defendants in court! In 1451 there was a trial of leeches: in 1120 a trial of caterpillars. Rats and mice were tried ad libitum. Sometimes these rodents would turn on their prosecutors and eat them alive, as they did to the Bishop of Widerolf in Strassburg, Germany, and to two Cologne bishops, Adolph and Guttengen, who were devoured in their castles on the Rhine. A historic rat trial is on record as having occurred at Anten, France, in 1531. The greatest criminal lawyer of the day defended the rodents. Twice he asked for a delay of the trial because his "clients" did not appear. Each time the court was moved with compassion over the barrister's clients, who were "old, feeble, sick, and lame," and couldn't come to court, he explained,

because "the streets were lined with cats." Whereupon the court ordered the owners of the cats to kill
them, so that the great barrister's clients could come
to court. But the owners of the cats couldn't catch
them, and so the rats were discharged! A sow and
six young pigs were tried in another case at Laveguy,
France, on the charge that they had murdered and
eaten a child. The lawyer for the pigs plead so eloquently for the young pigs, claiming that they did
not know what they were doing, that the Judge discharged them. But the sow was publicly executed!
In 1684 a vast flock of pigeons, devastating the grain-
fields of French Canada, were cited by the court to
appear for trial. The next day the flock continued
their flight to the South, and the efficiency of the
court's citation was everywhere proclaimed!

VI

"But, after all," commented my English host,
"you were not so far behind us in these notions, were
you?"

I couldn't deny it, for I had read "Gemmill" only
recently of what we in the United States achieved in
that line. It is almost incomprehensible to the present-day reader to realize that we tried our best in
America to go the English record one better not only
by actually boiling people to death in oil by slow degrees, but that we buried many a man and woman

alive: that we even went so far as to put small tubes in the mouths of these unfortunates extending to the outer air, so as to prolong their torture. We did all this in Salem—and more. We condemn now and laugh at the blue laws of New England, but it must not be forgotten that it was these same laws that put a stop to the ghastly cruelties which were then rampant. We had a penchant for hanging people here as well as they did across the water. The record is unfortunately still in existence of how two Quaker preachers had their ears cut off and were railroaded out of town. Men and women were publicly whipped upon the flimsiest pretexts. One woman for wearing a silk hood. Another for wearing gold buttons. Over ten per cent of a community was whipped or shackled to iron chains during a year. The letter "B" was branded on both cheeks of a burglar with hot irons. Women's tongues were cleft in twain for gossiping. If a man gossiped, one of his ears was cut off. If the brim of a man's hat exceeded by a quarter of an inch the prescribed width, he was branded or whipped. When a man tired of his wife he just left her, and went away, and he and she married again and all was well. If a woman went insane (and the wonder is that so few did), she was possessed of the devil and was promptly hanged. If one woman "bad-wished" another, she was publicly whipped, and the public whippers, the chroniclers say, were certainly kept busy. A group of ten girls was formed around a South Sea woman who taught them to tell fortunes. From that point on the ten girls became the oracles of the town. The fact that only two of the girls could write their own names, that two were epileptic and three were ordinary servants, made no difference. The girls were thought to be bewitched. They began to talk, and upon their silly prattle, accusing some of the best and most intelligent people of the town, twenty innocent persons were hanged and over two hundred imprisoned. If any one expressed the slightest sympathy with a prisoner or a victim that was hanged, he himself—or herself—was immediately executed.

VII

No, we were not "so far behind" England in these atrocious notions, sad to say!

"Well, those times are all over," I commented to my English friend.

"Yes," was his quiet comment, "Still, you do lynch people in America yet, don't you?"

It was my turn then to be quiet!

CHAPTER TWENTY
OVERHEARD

I really wonder where we got this idea: that the English have no sense of humor. They may not have the sense of the American type of broad humor, and this is, as I see it, no deprivation. But of true wit: I know not the equal of an Englishman's quick perception. And, when really witty, no nation better likes a story turned on itself for this supposed lack of humor than does the English. Yet, themselves, they are keenly fond of perpetuating this notion about themselves. They chuckle gleefully over it. In fact, they encourage it by asking, with twinkling eyes, if you know the real secret of making an Englishman happy in his old age.

If you say no, they will advise you, with glee:

"Tell him a story when he is young."

CHAPTER TWENTY
OVERHEARD

I

Two Americans who were on an Atlantic liner determined to make a test of an Englishman's sense of humor. They selected a very serious type of the Briton, and told him the most side-splitting story they could recall.

Never a smile did the Englishman crack, and the Americans were beside themselves in triumph over their test.

"That's all right, John," said one of the Americans, "you'll laugh over that next summer."

"Ah," replied the Englishman, "but I am sure I shan't, you know."

"Why not?" persisted the American.

"Well, you see," replied the still-serious Englishman, "I laughed over it last summer."

Seeing that the Americans took their defeat good-naturedly, the Englishman smilingly added "Now, let me tell you one."

"You see," he said, "we had not long ago quite a discussion in England over the possibility of removing some of the superfluous language from the Ten Commandments, in order to shorten Christ's ten injunctions. Quite a storm it was, you know.

"So it occurred to a reporter on one of the London papers to call on one of our leading Archbishops, and he asked if he believed that the Ten Commandments could be shortened.

" 'Yes, I think so,' was the Archbishop's inspired reply, and he didn't move a muscle in his face while he said: 'We might omit every *not* in the Commandments, and then, so as not to waste them, put them into the Creed.'

"The reporter thought he had a wonderful reply. And he had, you know. Only he didn't see the delicious humor of the idea. But his editor did!"

After the Americans had enjoyed to the full this story, one of them asked: "But doesn't that really prove a distinct lack of a sense of humor on the part of the reporter?"

"Quite so," replied the Briton. "I quite agree with you. But you see the editor was an Englishman."

"No, I meant the reporter who didn't see the humor," insisted the American.

"Yes, I know," smiled the Englishman as he started to walk down the deck. "But you see he was an American."

II

They can tell a few on the Americans, can these English when they're sure of their audience. A delicious one of this sort was told me by an Englishman

who was a "Tommy" in the great World War, and
he conceived a great friendship for an American buddy.
One day the two were at a religious service, and the
American boy listened with astonishment to a prayer
by a French chaplain.

"Well, that gets me," said Buddy.

"What's that?" asked Tommy.

"What good that fellow is doing in praying to
God in French."

It was this same British "Tommy" who told me
of an American "Buddy" stationed at Brest who decided to go to a dance given at the Y. M. C. A. hut.
Mrs. Vincent Astor, who was stationed there, came
to the same conclusion. It happened that the soldier
from Indiana arrived at the same time with Mrs.
Astor and, wanting to lose no time and seeing her
disengaged, not knowing her identity, asked her to
dance. Mrs. Astor at once consented. They had
taken only a few steps when the young soldier, impressed with his partner's dancing, said: "See here,
little one, you shake a pretty good little foot, you
do."

"Thanks," was the reply, "I'm glad you like my
dancing."

"I sure do. How about the next twirl?"

Mrs. Astor agreed, and this time he commented:
"You sure shake some shin, little blossom. I'd like
to see more of you. What may your name be?"

"Mrs. Vincent Astor," was the reply.

"That's right, kid," heartily answered the soldier. "That's right. Fly high, sis, fly high. Might as well kick high as kick low."

III

"You have, of course," said an Englishman to me, "seen the different names they give to inns on the road as you have motored by: 'The King's Arms,' 'The Prince of Wales's Arms,' and so on?"

I had.

"Well, the other day just out of Bournemouth a bobby arrested a terrible old sot. She looked as if she had been drunk for a year and steadily at that. When she was brought up before the Squire, the magistrate looked at what stood or rather was held up before him by two bobbies, and asked: "Who made this arrest?"

A bobby stepped forward. "I did, sir," he said.

"Where did you find her?" asked the magistrate.

"Dead drunk, sir, in 'The Prince of Wales's Arms,' sir."

IV

At an English luncheon, I happened to remark that Lord Birkenhead had just finished a visit to America.

"Ah, yes," said an Englishman at the table. "Did he tell you, by chance, of his experience when he was

Lord Chancellor of England and decided that he would make a personal investigation into the insane asylums which are, curiously enough, under the charge of the Lord Chancellor? Well, he selected an asylum adjacent to London, but was refused admission by the warder."

"But I must come in," persisted Lord Birkenhead. "I am the Lord Chancellor."

"Yes, I know, sir!" emphatically said the warder, and he repeated it as he closed the door, "I know, sir, but I have seven Lord Chancellors inside already."

"Wasn't that the same asylum," asked a woman at the table, "where one of the inmates was eternally walking and asking every one he met whether he had a piece of toast?"

"Why don't you rest, man?" said a visitor, "and why a piece of toast?"

The inmate looked at the visitor in surprise, and answered: "Why, don't you know? I am a poached egg, and want to sit down."

V

Which led another at the table to add to the gaiety of the luncheon by contributing this:

We had a very tense moment at a Sunday evening meal not long ago where I was unfortunately present. A noted General, a week-end guest, was present. The little girl of the household was at the table, and watched the General most intently, particularly when he drank. Finally, in a lull in the conversation, the little one could contain herself no longer.

"Muvvie?"

"Yes, dear," answered the mother. "What is it?" Fatal question!

With the table entirely quiet, she answered: "I have been watching the General at our meals, and he doesn't."

"Doesn't?" echoed the mother, while the General naturally was all attention.

"Doesn't what, dear?"

"Why, you said before he came that he drank like a fish."

VI

There was another child story told me: this time of an English lad of six who came to his mother and asked:

"Is it true, mother, than an apple a day keeps the doctor away?"

On being told it was, the boy went on:

"Well, I kept ten away this morning, but I think one will now have to come very soon."

Of course, the English have no end of yarns spun by the vicars of the parishes. This one, told me, impressed me as one of the best.

A widower sat dumb and disconsolate for days

after his wife's passing away. Their marriage had been long and apparently undimmed. The vicar of the parish, an old ally, called to cheer him up.

"My dear fellow," he said, "you must really rouse yourself. You must act in the spirit of your wife, who would never have countenanced such a torpor of dejection. Remember what a splendid wife she was in every way for all those forty years, what a model mother to your dear children."

The mourner still kept silence, but at length he broke it by saying:

"Thank you. She was all that you say. She *was* the most devoted wife and mother, the best of women, and for forty years not a harsh word passed between us."

Here he paused.

"But somehow," he proceeded, "somehow—I can hardly bring myself to say it—somehow, do you know, I never *liked* her."

VII

This, too, was told me with no end of chuckles.

A sister and brother, having a quarrel and finally getting uncontrollably angry, the brother told the sister to go to hell.

The sister told her father, and he remonstrated with the son.

"Why, father," he replied, "I didn't say anything

disrespectful to sis. I simply talked to her as a man would to his wife."

VIII

Of course, the English love to tell stories on the Scotch, with this, perhaps, as one of the best:

As an English railway train stopped at station after station, a Scotchman would rush out almost before the train stopped, and then rush back into the carriage almost breathless. Finally, after this had happened some dozen times, a fellow rider ventured to remark to the Scot:

"Pardon me, but do you think this rushing that you are doing at every station is good for your heart?"

When he could catch his breath the Scotchman replied: "That's just it, sir. It *is* my heart. My doctor says it is badly affected and that I may drop dead any moment. So you see, sir, I am buying a ticket from station to station."

IX

This story is told of Sir Henry Irving while he was touring the provinces one spring. Sir Henry had been out late—or early—the previous evening, and he came down into the public dining-room for a late breakfast.

Just as he was to taste his first dish, a large rat ran across the floor directly in the range of the actor's eye-line. Sir Henry returned the edible to the dish, made a grimace as of uncertainty, rubbed his monocle with a silk handkerchief, and proceeded once more to begin his breakfast—keeping his eye strictly on the place where he saw the rat.

At this, the understanding head-waiter came to the table and, bowing, said: "Pardon me, Sir Henry, it *was* a rat."

"Ah, so, thank you so much," replied the actor with a sigh of deep relief as he started in to enjoy his breakfast.

X

Speaking of Sir Henry reminds me of a story of Beerbohm Tree," said an English friend. "I had a really jolly experience with him one day when he was passing the week-end at our house, and we went out for a walk. We reached the little village Post Office. He looked at it for a moment, and said, "Let's go in."

"So this is the Post Office?" asked Sir Beerbohm of the young woman behind the grilled window, who replied that it was.

"Ah, yes," mused the actor. "And you sell postage stamps here?"

"Yes, sir," was once more the answer.

"May I see some?" asked Sir Beerbohm.

The girl looked a bit bewildered, but opening a drawer she pulled out a sheet of penny stamps.

"Ah," observed the actor, "and those are postage stamps, are they?"

"Yes, sir," was the reply, "penny stamps."

"Ah?" observed the actor, "all for a penny?"

"Oh, no, only one."

"So? Pretty, are they not?" observed Tree.

"Yes, sir," said the girl, becoming more and more bewildered.

"Do you sell these?" asked the actor.

"Why, yes," answered the girl.

"Just so. Just so," mused Tree. "I think that's a very pretty one: the one in the very centre. Will you just put your finger on it?"

The girl did so, and the actor said "Yes, that one. I will take that one, please," and taking a penny out of his pocket Tree, in the most dignified way, slid it under the grill and received the stamp, the girl's face full of surprise.

"Nice young woman that," observed Tree, as we walked on. "It was really a pleasure to buy something from her."

And never a smile did he crack!

XI

I was sending a telegram to a friend in Ealing.

"Ever hear of the cockney who wanted to send a telegram to Ealing, and was asked by the operator to spell it?" asked my English friend, standing by.

I had not.

"Well, this is the way he said it to the operator:

" 'Ere it is, miss:

E for 'Enery:
A wot a 'orse heats:
L where you goes to:
I wot you sees with:
N wot lays an hegg: and
G for 'is Majesty, King George the Fifth."

XII

It was this same friend who was telling me of a friend of his who had experienced rather a bad spill with his motor-car a few days before. He was a reckless driver, but this was unknown to his Uncle whom he took out for a ride in a new car. He lost entire control of the car, and it crashed into a tree and knocked both men out. The boy quickly scrambled to his feet, and going to his Uncle, who was brushing off his clothes, said: "By Jove, Uncle, I am all kinds of sorry to have spilled you like this, old top."

"Oh, it's all right, son," was the reply. What puzzles me is how you stop your car when there are no trees handy."

Which reminds me of another English story of a driver whose car got out of hand, crashed into a telegraph pole, broke the car to pieces, and left the man on the ground with his face and hands pretty badly cut.

Another car came up, stopped, and the driver got out and approached the man with one of those amazingly apt questions: Have an accident?"

"No, thanks," answered the man on the ground, looking up. "Just had one."

With the most delicious chuckle, they will tell you in England of an old lady who, when she rode in an automobile, became deeply exercised about her safety in the car. So, one day, as she was driving behind what had been represented to her as a particularly careful chauffeur, she asked: "Now, my man, tell me this: When you see another car deliberately coming right at you, what do you do?"

"Well, my lady," soberly answered the driver, "I always stop immediately, get out, take the car apart and hide all the pieces in the grass."

This one, too, they tell:

A man wanting a new horn for his automobile was asked by the dealer: "Do you wish one that makes a particularly loud noise, sir?"

"No," answered the purchaser, "I would like one that really sneers!"

XIII

An English friend had just returned from a hunting trip in Alaska, and had been present at this delightful tête-à-tête between an American girl and the keeper of a fox-farm which she had been looking over.

After admiring a beautiful silver specimen, she asked the keeper: "Just how many times can the fox be skinned for his fur?"

"Three times, miss," said the keepr gravely. "Any more than that would spoil his temper."

This must have been a difficult position even for a criminal in a famous London trial, as pictured by a London paper:

All during the testimony he hardly moved in his chair.
For the most of the time he rested his head on his chin.

They tell this story of a green-goods man, as they call a grocer in England. His name was March. One day the butcher came around and said: "March, the first of April the price of meat's going up."

"That's all right," said March.

A day or two later the wholesale jobber's salesman came along. "March, the first of April the price of sugar is going up."

"That's all right," said March.

A few days later the landlord came around and said: "March, the first of April the rent's going up."

"All right," said March.

A few days later March put up a sign in his window:

THE FIRST OF APRIL WILL BE THE
END OF MARCH

An excellent yarn was told by a member of a Manchester firm which had written to a London mercantile house asking what information it could give about a young fellow who had applied for a job with the firm. The London firm wrote back: "We know Mr. J. to be excellently connected and well bred. His grandfather was General S., a cousin of the fourth Lord G. His mother was P., and so related to the Countess of H."

Whereupon the Manchester firm replied: "Thank you very much for your letter in regard to Mr. J. We would state, however, that the young man is required for clerical work: not for breeding purposes."

Another good story I was told was of a woman who attended a Wesleyan prayer-meeting at a small town in England, and when the pastor of the church asked those who would like to be remembered in the prayers of the congregation to declare themselves and their desires for prayer, she got up and requested prayers for herself: for divine guidance, prosperity, and relief from eczema!

XIV

It was at this same gathering that my neighbor at table, replying to a friend's question about her mother's health, answered: "Poor dear, she has such an attack of Framboesia." I made no comment, but here was a word which I had associated in my mind with raspberries from the Dutch word Frambosa, and

that at another time I had thought of as a perfume
—only to find, from the Oxford dictionary, that it
was the name of a skin-disease!

It made me realize that you cannot always depend
upon the way a word or a phrase sounds, as when a
lecturer, speaking of the surrender of Lee to Grant,
sent his audience into a roar of laughter by saying
that at the historic meeting while General Lee wore
the full uniform of a Southern General, General Grant
had nothing on but a Union suit!

An apt phrase was used at this gathering by a Peer,
who, after listening to a guest who was bemoaning
the state of general conditions in England, and who
concluded that "everything seemed to be wrong," replied: "Ah, that is just what makes the situation so
deucedly awkward, you know, because, as Charles
Reade said: 'Everything is the one thing that won't
stand being set to rights.'"

I had to go to England to have an apt American
phrase brought to me. "Do you know, your Leopold
Godowsky, the pianist, gave a very happy definition
the other day when he said that 'Talent is evolution,
and genius is revolution'? Deuced clever that—and
what's more, it's true, you know."

HARD-EARNED WAGES

The English were laughing hilariously over the
story of an Irishman employed in repairing the prop-
erties of an old chapel in Ireland, being refused pay-

ment in lump, was asked for details, and sent in his
bill as follows:

Corrected the Ten Commandments.............	5.6.
Embellished Pontius Pilate and put new ribbons on his bonnet............................	5.6.
Put a new tail on the Rooster of St. Peter and mended his comb.......................	10.6.
Revarnished and gilded the left wing of the Guardian Angel...............................	4.6.
Washed the servant of the High Priest and put carmine on his cheeks....................	5.6.
Renewed Heaven, adjusted two stars, and cleaned the moon...............................	7.10.
Put five additional rays to the sun.............	5.0.
Renewed the flames of Hell, and put a new tail on the devil, mended his hoof, and did several odd jobs for the d——d..................	7.10.
Rebordered the robe of Herod and adjusted his wig	4.0.
Put new spotted dashes on the son of Tobias....	6.0.
Cleaned the ears of Balaam's ass and shod him....	3.2.
Put new ear-rings into the ears of Sarah.........	2.4.
Repainted Noah's Ark, put a new stone in David's sling, enlarged the head of Goliath and extended his legs...........................	3.0.
Put a new shirt on the Prodigal Son............	3.0.
Total...................................	£3.15.11.

CHAPTER TWENTY–ONE

WHEN THE ENGLISH ADVERTISE

I determined now to devote myself to reading the important news of the day when, on my way to the newspages, I met some for-sale advertisements of castles and estates.

There was no passing them over.

CHAPTER TWENTY-ONE
WHEN THE ENGLISH ADVERTISE

I

I WANTED to buy a different castle or estate every day. First it was an historic castle built when England was young, with a small strip of land consisting of a mere 24,000 acreage!

Then it was an estate "decorated and furnished throughout by the Brothers Adam." *That* was a buy. Not much land: only 6,000 acres!

There was only one thing that consistently held me back. It was the disturbing fly in an otherwise perfect ointment. I confess that I like my bath. And so far as I could see the architects of these wonderful castles and estates didn't bathe themselves, and were determined that their clients shouldn't bathe either.

The 24,000-acre castle, for example, was wonderful. It had a moat, and it had turrets: battlements, in fact. There was a real drawbridge, built in the thirteenth century and "still in perfect order." The great hall was 140 feet long: the drawing-rooms were four: dining-rooms three: the woodwork was all old, of superb panels, and of bedrooms there were 34. But there were only 2 bathrooms—one a master's bath-room and the other for the 34 guests.

II

So it was with the others:

"A beautiful estate . . . had 18 bedrooms and 2 bath-rooms." You could but wonder what the other 16 occupants did.

"Wonderful oak-panelled halls . . . 10 bedrooms: 1 tiled-bath."

"Delightfully arranged house . . . 7 chambers: commodi-ous bathroom." Surely the inference here could not be intended.

"Superb estate . . . 2 conservatories: 3 reception-rooms: 2 dining-rooms: 9 bedrooms, bathroom." Everything taken care of in pairs and numbers, apparently, with the "tub" in the singular!

"Residential estate . . . 4 reception-rooms: oak-panelled corridors: beautifully decorated, 2 dining-rooms, break-fast rooms and grapery: 4 conservatories: master's bed-room, with dressing-room and fully-equipped bath attached: 14 other bedrooms. Perfectly equipped house,"—for the master, yes. Of course, this was on the sea; still, the ocean *is* a bit chilly for bathing in winter, even for your hardy Britisher!

The choice one appeared when "one of the most sumptuous estates in the British Isles" was offered for sale. It consisted of 1,891 acres. It advertised itself as having "4 reception-rooms, 3 drawing-rooms, 3 dining-rooms, 2 billiard rooms," and, as a finishing touch, "a separate private chapel building for week-end guests," which I thought was a most considerate provision. Certainly the material and the spiritual had been most carefully looked after, but the fly in the ointment was still there: "23 bedrooms and 3 bathrooms"!

III

The estate which absorbed me, and has ever since I read of it, was "one of the most historic places in England, dating back to 1182." The advertisement recited very carefully how the greatest care had been taken by the present owner and his ancestors to leave the "castle" as near to its original condition as possible, "consistent with modern living and conveniences." Which latter fact was particularly observed in connection with one feature of the "castle." The present owner had suspected for some time that there existed some "subterranean dungeons" under the castle, "and so, at considerable expense, he had dug down and finally uncovered them, only to discover the bones of fifteen skeletons, with one skeleton in a sitting posture. This latter skeleton is complete. There is every reason to believe that these dungeons represent the twelfth century." Then, with a consideration that is really exhilarating, the announcement concludes: "The owner has left the skeletons exactly as he discovered them, and the present beautiful dining-room is built directly over the dungeons, constituting a unique feature of this wonderful estate." I agree with the uniqueness of the owner's achievement, but whether the daily joy of dining over a dungeon of skeletons is exactly a selling point does admit of at least a doubt. But some one evidently thought so, for a week afterward I read that the estate had been sold—and I dislike to record it: "to a wealthy American." My mind became so fixed on the dungeons and the sitting skeleton and his brothers —and maybe sisters—that I never looked to see how many bathrooms "the wealthy American" had bought."

IV

I made a determined resolution now that I must divorce my attention from the advertisements. But it was not an easy matter to tear one's self loose from them. For instance, here was one that held out a most attractive experience if one should fall ill. The alluring advertisement ran:

This Nurses' Home makes a specialty of nurses of attractive appearance, sunny disposition, and immaculate in their raiment. Special attention is given to gentlemen's nervous disturbances.

It sounded far more enticing than did an advertisement of a Dancing Academy which promised that "we positively teach any one 'The Blues' in one lesson."

There was an attractive note, too, in the advertisement which advertised "a self-contained flat in London"—principally because, I presume, I always liked every one and everything to be self-contained.

Then, as to the advertisements of birds and animals, they beguiled me almost to the point of wildest purchase. I could scarcely restrain myself from buying several of Lieutenant-Colonel Richardson's pedigreed airedales. They appeared to be wonderfully trained to do everything but talk, but they were particularly valuable " for burglars and ladies walking alone."

V

Then those African parrots! Every day I read a different advertisement about their marvellous talking qualities—"just like some humans"—which I thought was not altogether beguiling as one or two pictures of talking humans came to mind. However, when the skilful bird-keeper finally got hold of an African parrot which "has a vocabulary of fully 1,000 words, with each word distinctly spoken," I almost fell for the bird, until a friend assured me, who had heard the visitor from Africa, that fully one-half of the 1,000 words were not fit for polite ears! But the advertisement did not state this latter accomplishment.

I don't know exactly what the lady in Hampshire had in mind when she offered, as an inducement to let her house, that the lessee could enjoy "tea and grounds." I have always thought that people liked their tea without grounds.

VI

As for the numerous advertisements offering to "turn suits and make them look as good as new"—a relic of war times, I take it—it was with positive difficulty that I refrained from having all my suits turned, whether they needed it or not. There was just one note in the advertisements which restrained me: "Guaranteed absolutely invisible," they promised. I thought, upon reflection, that this might be a distinct disadvantage with a suit of clothes, whether it was on or off.

VII

This was to me an interesting advertisement:

Clean dancing at The —— Margate every evening except Monday.

Which, of course, brought a record-breaking crowd on Monday!

It was at this same resort, Margate, that an old

custodian of the bathhouses had an uncomfortable habit of entering the houses sometimes before the occupants had entirely reclothed themselves.

Finally a young woman bather said: "John, you ought to knock before you come in. Some day you might come in while I was undressed."

To which the honest old soul replied: "Lor' bless you, miss! no danger of that. I allus peeks through the knot-hole afore I comes in."

VIII

Speaking of advertisements, this story told me by the local bookstore owner himself is extremely neat.

A teamster wandered into this bookstore during the strike, and presently, showing signs of displeasure, started for the door.

"What's the matter?" asked a clerk. "Don't you see what you want?"

"I came in here looking for work," said the man. "But I see on that pile o' books: 'Dickens Works Here All This Week for Ten Shillings.' He can if he wants to, but I won't."

Sometimes there is tragedy as well as unconscious humor in an advertisement:

Spiritualistic fortune-telling, free love and soul mating having broken up my home, will sell steel-top six-hole range with coil, gas water heater and other furniture. Call 9 to 7.

IX

For an original "selling-point" this sign in an English restaurant window is difficult to beat:

If your wife can't cook, don't divorce her. Eat here and keep her as a pet.

This advertisement was certainly questionable:

Ladies and gentlemen who will call and have left off wearing apparel will receive highest prices at Mrs. ——, —— Street.

This was a want advertisement:

Wanted: A girl of fifteen, with much experience in life, to look after child.

Another:

Desired: A literary man. Must have profound knowledge of the classics to write advertisements for a new mouthwash.

This sounded like a call for a champion woman pedestrian:

Christlike Gentleman would like Christlike Lady to walk with him through life.

I wonder what must have been the thoughts of the parties to this brief but startling announcement:

Mr. and Mrs. J. F. Cavanagh regret to announce the marriage of their daughter, Edith Avegne, to Lieutenant Weymouth Cole.

X

I began now to notice a class of advertisements under the birth and death notices which we know not of in our American life. This one, as an example, on the anniversary of the passing of Lord Northcliffe:

NORTHCLIFFE.—In ever grateful and affectionate memory of my chief, VISCOUNT NORTHCLIFFE.

There has never been any one just like him before and there never will be again, and the world is the poorer for his death.

Again, on Sir Henry Irving's anniversary day:

Henry Irving—I loved him then and I love him now.

On Mr. Gladstone's day:

Gladstone—How you are missed in this wrongly-directed empire of ours!

To George Meredith:

MEREDITH, George. Not forgotten.

Rather pretty custom, I thought.

CHAPTER TWENTY-TWO

ARE ENGLISH NEWSPAPERS DULL?

I certainly cannot agree with those Americans who find the English newspapers "dull." In point of fact, their contents kept me so busy that I found almost my entire days devoted to their reading with full enjoyment.

ARE ENGLISH NEWSPAPERS DULL?

I

For instance, I should not consider this paragraph exactly "dull":

A young lady advertises in a contemporary print for a husband, and states that she will "walk for half an hour, on next Sunday, the 26th inst., at 3 o'clock p. m., on the north side of Merrion-square, prepared to receive any written communication that may be handed to her. In order that she may be easily distinguished . . . she begs to describe her dress:—She will wear a leghorn bonnet, white lace veil, with a plume of white feathers, and a green silk opera cloak lined with white sarcenet, a swansdown muff, and a black velvet reticule with a steel clasp, which will be open to receive any billet that may, by proper dexterity, be dropped into it."

Or take this "close up" of a bit of English domestic life:

Mrs. C—— K—— is near death from a shotgun wound, her son, Benjamin, 22, is in a critical condition from knife wounds, and her husband, 65, is badly cut over the face and hands and is under arrest as a result of a free for all family fight Wednesday at their home near B——, in which a daughter, Lida, 17, also engaged. The argument is said to have started in a disagreement as to where the family

should spend a holiday. The mother and children wanted
to go up the creek for a picnic, and the father wanted to go
down the creek. The husband is alleged to have shot his
wife in the back with a shotgun loaded with two ball bear-
ings. The husband then was attacked by his son, who was
wounded by a large knife cut which severed one rib. Coming to her brother's rescue, Lida, the daughter, beat the
father off with a heavy plank.

Then, the chronicle gravely adds:

The picnic had to be postponed.

II

The next day the same paper told of a delicious sign
in an English office showing, in more than that of the
joke which it was intended to be, the contrast between
the English and American business methods.

This Englishman had gotten a sign in America reading:

DO IT NOW! DON'T WAIT TILL TOMORROW!

He brought it home, put it over his desk, but not
until he had crossed out the American slogan and
printed underneath:

DON'T DO IT NOW! THINK FIRST, AND DO IT
TOMORROW!

Which reminded the writer of an excellent "to-
morrow" story: that of the English manufacturer
who, in the period of the war depression, went to his

bank and secured a loan of £5,000. The loan did not suffice, and when he had exhausted the loan he sought the bank and asked for an additional £2,000.

"We cannot do it," voted the directors, and the manufacturer asked the privilege of speaking to the directors at their next meeting.

He repeated his request, and again he was refused.

Looking around the table he asked: "Do you gentlemen know anything about the cracker business?"

The reply of all was in the negative.

"Well," said the manufacturer, "you will to-morrow morning when I turn it over to you."

III

I became positively thrilled now in a discussion which waged furiously, even to the extent of a long editorial, in one of the papers about the momentous question of whether a fox wags his tail with pleasure the same as a dog. I could not quite make out which side of this discussion got the better of it, whether the fox or the dog won out. Neither, I should judge, could the editor, for after the letters, pro and con, had filled some eighteen of his broad, long columns, he announced that the discussion was at an end and no further letters could be published. But it was astonishing how the discussion took hold of the English imagination, for wherever you went some one would start: "Have you seen that jolly discussion about whether a fox wags his tail the same as a dog? Now, when I was in Australia—" and one hunting yarn would remind some one present of another, and before the evening was over I couldn't for the life of me see what experiences with kangaroos and bears and wild cats and panthers had to do with the far more absorbing question of those tails of the fox and the dog!

IV

I found myself getting very much interested, too, in the "visitations" (whatever they were I could not find out) and meetings of The Worshipful Order of Skinners. That name appealed tremendously to me, and I wondered how it happened that such an organization had escaped us in America. The "Worshipful" part of such an organization might present some difficulties with us, but I should think there would be an easy and large membership for the "Skinners" part.

I was impressed, too, with an American chance to emulate an English custom at public meetings. For instance, when it was announced that Mr. Israel Zangwill will speak, and Mr. Leslie Laurence will support him. There are so many of our public speakers who need to be supported while speaking. There was a delicious irony in the error which a London Sunday paper made when it promised of this same meeting that: "Mr. Zangwill will speak, and Mr. Leslie Laurence will suppress him." We could find an easy application of that idea in America—particularly in Washington!

V

An interesting item in a London newspaper was this:

The Americans have gotten far away from the better customs of their ancestors. The American Indian, for instance, showed the American the economy of fuel by building a small fire and sitting close to it, while the American of to-day builds a large fire and sits far away from it.

This audacious bit was in an Egyptian letter:

The difference between an Egyptian snake and the well-known Egyptian flea is that the snake crawls on its own stomach, while the flea is not so particular.

The same paper contained a story of Rachmaninoff, the pianist, concerning his well-known impatience with the popularity of his famous Prelude. So many questions are asked him about this composition that on one occasion when an English woman he had just met questioned him as to whether he had had in his mind any particular incident or scene when he composed that Prelude, he answered solemnly:

"Yes, madame, I had in mind a woman buried alive and knocking at the coffin frantically to get out."

VI

A fascinating habit of *The London Times* is to give each day a brief pen-picture of the outstanding event of the same day a hundred years ago. The "outstanding event" of one day seemed to have been this:

A certain lady in high life is now pursued by no less than *three* Marquises!

It is interesting to note, as an aside, that at this time the daily price of *The Times* was 7 pence: about 14 cents, according to present rates of exchange. From this doubtless came the habit, which prevails to-day at the 2 pence daily rate, of one copy of *The Times* being passed from hand to hand until it supplied the news reading of an entire village!

VII

The difference between the athletic training of English boys and girls was well illustrated in these two items. The first was apropos of an afternoon of sports:

Twelve Eton boys, all belonging to prominent families, now competed for the afternoon's principal prize, by rolling tennis-balls with their noses.

But the English girl must be given a more strenuous form of athletic training—at least one would think so from this item:

William K—— of —— Street was taken to the ——
Hospital yesterday afternoon having had six teeth knocked
out and his jaw seriously fractured by being kicked in the
face by a girl friend.

At the same time, they have a distinct sense in England of protecting their girlhood, since almost the
entire police force of one county was called into action
to arrest an automobile which bore on its tire-cover
this legend:

FOLLOW ME, CHICKENS, I'M FULL OF CORN

An English lady, full of concern for her sex, told in
a "letter" of the very skilful manner in which she had
had her hair cut:

Every hair was very carefully cut, singeing each hair
afterward so as to close up the ends. This is very important,
as it prevents the catching of a cold in the head through the
open ends of the hairs.

VIII

A very much perturbed Englishman wrote to ask
the editor if he could tell him where he lived. He said
his home was in a district in Surrey. But his postal
district was Esher, and local rates went to Thames
Ditton. Parliamentary vote, he explained, goes to
Chertsey. Municipal vote goes to East Molesey.
Electric light comes from Twickenham. Gas comes
from Kingston. Water is supplied by the Metro-

politan Water Board. and telephone exchange is Molesey.

"Now, can you tell me where I live?" asked the correspondent.

But the editor was silent.

This item, however, made the editor vocal:

Dating from 1150, St. Dunstan's, Cranbrook (Kent), has a quaint local wedding custom. When a bridal couple leave the church, their way is strewn with emblems, denoting the bridegroom's calling. Thus, in place of confetti, a carpenter's bride walks upon shavings, a butcher's treads upon sheep-skins, a shoemaker's upon odd pieces of leather, a baker's upon bread-crumbs, and a greengrocer's upon cabbage leaves.

"All very well," came from the editor. "But now suppose a dentist or a barber marries, then what? We hesitate at the thought of what the custom might do in the case of an undertaker!"

IX

No newspapers can be regarded as "dull" which present these items over a brief period.

CHAPTER TWENTY-THREE
AMERICANA

I do not wish to be misunderstood as writing in criticism of these great English papers. Quite the contrary. I cannot join in the American idea that these papers are "heavy" and "uninteresting." Not if read aright. I found them positively exciting. Too much so. Then they certainly leave little to be desired in the excellent English with which correspondents and editors alike tell what they see and think. If good writing be "dull," then I like dullness. But what one cannot help deploring, however, is their American misinformation and inaccuracies, for most of which there is no excuse.

CHAPTER TWENTY-THREE
AMERICANA

I

WHAT I mean by American misinformation, which is absolutely inexcusable, is such a paragraph as the following:

A gigantic bridge has been planned to cross the famous Golden Gate at the entrance to San Francisco harbor. At the top of the great steel towers it is proposed to build platforms from which visitors will be able to obtain a marvellous view of San Francisco and the mighty Atlantic.

Certainly an amazing ocular feat.

Take another statement: that President Coolidge "embarked on the *Mayflower* at New York for a week-end sail down the Potomac."

II

Surely the name of former Secretary of State Hughes should be familiar enough in his diplomatic relations with Great Britain. Yet when he arrived in England, in scarcely a single instance was his middle initial of E correctly given. It was Charles F. Hughes, or Charles M. or Charles S. As to his record, the ignorance was nothing short of abysmal. I will spare

the name of the leading London paper which said that
Mr. Hughes was a former Ambassador to the Court
of Saint James's. This caught the eye of a rival editor,
who sought to set his brother-editor right by assuring
him that Mr. Hughes was never Ambassador to the
Court of Saint James's, but that "Mr. Hughes was
formerly Chief Justice of the Supreme Court and now
held the important post of private secretary to President Coolidge"!

When Henry W. Taft visited London, he was
promptly ticketed as "the son of the former President
and now Justice of the Supreme Court of New York."

General Dawes was "a prominent banker of New
York," and to palliate Chicago because it had taken
away its most prominent citizen, it referred, in the
same issue, to Harvard University at Chicago.

The Sesquicentennial celebration (at Philadelphia)
was being held on "the banks of the Potomac."

The air mail from New York to Chicago was referred
to as covering a nightly distance of 3,000 miles.

The *Leviathan* was being cleaned "at the largest
dry-dock on the Hudson River at Boston."

III

There is another form of Americana which, rather
than committed by them, is imposed upon them, all
too frequently. I found an apt illustration of this

Americana in a peculiarly American convention which was held in London while I was there. There were some thousand or more Americans—of a certain type —in this convention, and a little habit which is characteristic of this type of the American began immediately upon arrival.

The day following the arrival of this modest company was Sunday, and one contingent attended service at Westminster Abbey, another at Saint Paul's Cathedral. The following morning the habit broke out. A member from Texas began with the quiet statement about the Abbey that "we were tremendously impressed with your national Valhalla. But, then, you know, with the memorials to Washington and Lincoln and Longfellow and Lowell and Page we claim it as much our own as much as you do."

And that was that! The fact that the Abbey is not a national Valhalla at all, and that no one ever before found a bust or tablet of either Washington or Lincoln did not trouble the gentleman from Texas for a moment.

The Saint Paul Cathedral delegation had their spokesman, too, and he was not to be outdone. It was superb," he said the next day to a reporter. "But then we are not strangers to it, you know. We know Saint Paul's and your Dean Inge so well we feel that both belong to us as much as they do to you."

Thus both edifices were appropriated.

IV

The next day the Prince of Wales was bodily appropriated. "He is a wonder," burst forth an officer of the Association. "But then we know him and love him as much in America as you do, and we claim him as our own."

Thus, in a sentence, the future King of England was Americanized.

The King came next. The English, no doubt, felt that he might be allowed to be regarded as a British possession. But not so. A delegate from Missouri attended to him after seeing him at a public function, and in this picturesque fashion he went into the American bag. "He is a bird, all right. I went right up to him and shook hands with him, and he smiled and said: 'I am always glad to meet Americans.' Wasn't it quick of him to know that I was an American? He is a regular fellow, he is. He ought to be in America, he ought. He would feel at home there." And so the "bird" was Missouried!

V

It remained now for an American woman to clear up the throne and appropriate Queen Mary with the remark that "she might as well be an American, we know her so well," and then adding the sage remark: "She would be happy over there, too. We'd make a

tremendous fuss over her in Texas," which must have
sounded very attractive to Her Majesty as a contrast
to Buckingham Palace!

"Isn't it a bit odd, though," asked a bewildered
Englishman to me, when he saw his King, Queen, the
Heir Apparent and his two cathedrals appropriated,
"that a people who fought so strenuously against the
idea of monarchy should now be so attracted by the
same institution which once they thoroughly de-
spised?"

But a climax was imminent, and it was left for a
New Yorker to really finish the job. To his large
mind these specific and individual appropriations
seemed unworthy of American enterprise. So he
came out with this delicate statement: "Of course,
London is a great city. But it is just as much American as it is English. Look at the Americans here:
see how our business interests are here: the position
of our financiers: how you depend upon our gold.
That is why it is so great. London is rapidly beginning to belong to America: an annex to New York,
so to speak"!

An Englishman, reviewing the devastating appropriations, commented to me: "When your people
appropriate, they do it in a large way, don't they?"

"Never mind," I encouraged, "you have the rest
of England—as yet."

"Ah," he returned, "but I am not so sure of that

An American told me yesterday that Stratford-on-Avon had become an American shrine. So that appears to be included, too!"

VI

Who was it that said the English have no sense of humor?

VII

Another form of Americana is also extremely unpleasant to hear: the stories which are repeated in every part of London over the frantic attempts of American women to be "presented at Court." It is difficult to conceive of any ground, except a gratification of the silliest vanity, on which an American woman should desire a Court presentation. To the English woman there is a distinct advantage in being on what is called the King's visiting list. It gives her entrée to Court functions, a presence at Ascot, and other privileges which to the resident woman are advantages where emphasis is placed on such perquisites. But the American woman, living in the United States, gains none of these privileges: she has not the opportunity to enjoy them. Hence what is the advantage to her of a presentation? the English ask, and wisely so. As a matter of fact, we fought valiantly to eliminate from American life and shores the very thing which is now so industriously courted. For industrious are these women to an unbelievable point. Nor is it a question of here and there an American woman, but it is a case literally of hundreds who, each year as the presentation season approaches, make the life of the American Ambassador at the Court of Saint James's miserable with their insistent importunities. One has only to be in the confidence of some one close to the inside of the American Embassy at London to feel ashamed and grow hot with indignation at the lengths to which scores of American women will go in order to secure the Ambassador's recognition. Every political, social, business influence is sought and brought to bear by these women upon the Embassy, and for weeks and months this bombardment goes on.

VIII

Women seem to lose all sense of self-respect and shame in this mad desire for royal recognition. And pray what does it amount to when achieved? I was amused not long ago to have a Western woman describe to me the cordial manner in which King George and Queen Mary had shaken hands with her at her presentation, and what Their Majesties had said to her. She had evidently repeated this so often that she had come to believe it herself, since it is, of course, known to every one conversant with the customs of Court circles that the King and Queen never shake hands with those present, but, seated on a throne, simply nod in recognition of the curtsey of the one presented. Then why this deception? Why this struggle for a custom absolutely un-American and foreign to every American institution? The most unintelligent part of the whole proceeding is when an American woman is given the opportunity of presentation, she almost invariably gives the impression to her friends that it is either "at the King's or Queen's own request" that she is presented, or that she has been "asked" or "urged" by the American Ambassador. And this after months of frantic effort and every form of wire-pulling to attain the coveted opportunity!

"These women make the Americans, as a whole, seem so unjustly ridiculous in the eyes of English gentlefolk," said an attaché of the American Embassy. "An American is covered with confusion when this subject is brought up at an English dinner."

IX

It is devoutly to be wished that American tourists would not attempt to air their opinions on subjects concerning which the English are so well posted, and on which our lack of information is often lamentable. Take the question of the great out-of-doors. It is as difficult to find an Englishman who does not know his flowers or his birds as it is to meet an American who does know them.

I was at a dinner at which a Philadelphia woman was present and, owing to her prominence, her remarks were listened to with attention. She told the story of what seems to be known in Philadelphia as "the Academy bat"—a creature known to every Philadelphian as housing itself somewhere in the rafters of the roof of the stage of the Academy of Music, and generally choosing the most gala opera night for its annual flight over the brilliantly lighted stage and the darkened atmosphere—much to the terror of the women with coiffures especially "dressed" for the occasion. This woman said that the "Academy bat" has all of thirty years to its credit. Although the entire stage crew turns out after the bat's annual appearance, its habitat has thus far eluded the most agile climber and the strongest flash-light. I saw the eyes of the English part of the company open widely at this tale of the age of the bat. The listeners became even more open-eyed when "the lady from Philadelphia" eloquently told, with convincing truth, the legend that a bat's favorite resting-place is in the soft meshes of a woman's hair, whereas, of course, no one has ever been found who has seen a bat seek such a trysting-place. But the climax came when she referred to the bat as being "a blind bird" or "a vermin-infested bird," or this kind or that sort of a bird.

X

When the lady rested her story with the English gathering I waited for the reaction that I was certain would come.

It did—and almost instantly, too.

"Very interesting," was the comment of a man in the group, "very. But I have often noticed that the Americans and your newspapers, too, speak of the bat as a bird. Why is that, may I ask?"

I saw that the lady from Philadelphia was distinctly up a tree!

"You do not class the bat as a bird, then, in England?" I broke in.

I saw that the American woman was clearly at a disadvantage.

"Well, hardly," was the reply. "Do you, may I ask?"

I mumbled a reply distinctly inaudible. It was at least my place to protect my countrywoman.

"No," continued the Englishman, "a bat is not a bird. It is no more a bird than is a flying squirrel. A bat is a distinct mammal, the only resemblance between a bat and a bird being that because of a bat's fore limbs being so modified as to form wings, it is capable of flying—being the only mammal capable of true flight."

All the same, I thought, let any ten persons in an

American group begin to talk about bats, and before long nine of them, if not all ten, will refer to a bat as a bird!

XI

An American girl of the pensive type was being conducted through a beautiful English garden by the head-gardener, and was passing under a three-hundred-year-old tree of gigantic proportions.

With a poetic raising of the eyes she turned to the gardener and said: "Oh, if this wonderful beech could speak, what do you think it would say?"

"I don't exactly know, miss," replied the gardener. "But it might say that it is not a beech but an oak."

An Englishman, passionately fond of his flowers, was showing an American visitor through his garden when the woman exclaimed: "What a wonderful flower," pointing to a superb bush.

"Yes," replied the host. "It surprises many. It belongs to the begonia family."

"Oh," commented the woman, "not yours, then. But how charming of you to tend it while the family is away."

A Dean famous for his roses all through England was showing a rose, grown to perfection, to an American.

"Have you ever seen a more perfect bloom?" he asked.

"Very nice indeed," replied the lady from Illinois. "But you forget, Dean, that America is really the home of beautiful roses. We had them twice this size."

"Ah?" replied the Dean as he turned and escorted his visitor to the house.

XII

Nor is this knowledge and love of flowers confined to the "upper classes," as they are called in England. It goes straight down the line to the humblest worker, who has his little garden, and is always at work in it when he is not at his daily task.

I wonder, for instance, how many waiters, chauffeurs, and hotel porters in America would know the flowers. I thought of this one day when tea was being served in an English garden, and the waiter said to me: "Excuse me, sir, but don't you think the effect of those roses on the arbor is very beautiful?" and, as I looked up to see where he was pointing, I saw his face fairly alive with pleasure. Upon another occasion, I happened to observe to a butler that the weather was rather cold for July. "It is, sir," he replied, "and the worst of it is, the flowers do not bloom as they should. And of course if there are no flowers there isn't much, is there, sir?" We were starting out on a ride in rural England when our chauffeur said: "When we get a bit down this road, sir, you will see a very

beautiful sight if you will look to the right." Naturally, I thought of some beautiful old priory, or old
house, or ruin. But soon we came to a nurseryman's
rosery, and the chauffeur turned round, with his face
full of pleasure, and beckoned to us to see. We had
been driving through a wonderful rhododendron plan-
tation, with plants fifteen to twenty feet high, and I
didn't imagine there could be a rhododendron plant-
ing in the world more beautiful. "Ah," said the
chauffeur, "you should have seen it some five years
ago when there was a complete belt of these rhodo-
dendrons, so that on both sides you had a bloom you
could never forget once you saw it."

"What became of those?" I asked.

The face became flushed with heat. "Would you
believe it? They cut them down just as if they were
weeds. Think of it, sir, cutting down such beautiful
things!"

"I tell you, sir," said the hotel porter, who had been
standing by, "something ought to be done to a man
who would do such a thing. Let a rhododendron or a
may hedge or a tree stand in the way where these
criminals—yes, sir, I think they are criminals—want
to build something, and down comes plant or hedge or
tree."

And for five minutes these two men argued back
and forth as to what could be done with these "building criminals who respected nothing!"

"You can't match it for beauty, now can you, sir?" said an ordinary laborer to me, as we met in a path where a superb yucca was in full bloom. "God certainly knows how to make a flower, doesn't he, though?"

I agreed, and the man went on his way, his face aglow with the beauty of a flower which many an owner of an American estate would not know by name.

Truly England would not be England without its flowers and those who know and love them.

XIII

I wish, too, we could not use such exaggerated figures in our talk. Small figures seem to be offensive to the American. We use large figures very lightly in our talk.

An American and an Englishman had been attending a tennis tournament, and upon reaching home they were asked if, in view of the rain, the attendance had been large.

"Oh, yes," said the American. "There must have been 20,000 at least—don't you think so?" turning to the Englishman.

"Oh, did you think so?" returned the polite host. "I should have said there were hardly 3,000."

The next day the London *Times* deplored the small attendance of only 3,100!

"Over 85,000 persons attended the fight," said the
New York newspapers of a prize-fight in London at
the Wembley Stadium. The London *Times*, the next
day, complained of the smallness of the crowd: the
sale of tickets having reached less than 18,000!

XIV

An American was holding forth in an English company as to the unjust fares on the Pullman cars, and
spoke of them as "an imposition on a majority of the
American public."

"Oh," said a quiet Englishman, "I didn't realize
that so many of your people rode in Pullman cars."

"Yes, indeed," blithely answered the American,
"nearly everybody does."

"Ah, so?" commented the Englishman.

He knew perfectly well that not one-tenth of one
per cent of the American public ever uses Pullman
cars!

It is amazing how the tendency to exaggerate when
it comes to numbers seems to come all too easy to the
American mind.

An American woman accompanied her English
hostess to a concert in Queen's Hall only to say at
dinner how successful was the concert and that there
were fully 5,000 persons present. Yet if Queen's Hall
is given a capacity of 1,500 it is a generous estimate.

"I have received several hundred complaints

about" a certain matter, said a corporation official to me the other day. I was surprised. When the letters were produced they figured exactly 31 !

"Does it really matter?" asked a friend the other day when we were discussing this American trait.

I contended that the truth always mattered, particularly to the English mind, which is rarely given to exaggeration, and whose people are apt to be led to an uncomfortable questioning of American figures.

"You always speak in such large figures," said an English merchant to me.

And he might well have added but for his politeness: "And not always truthful figures."

CHAPTER TWENTY-FOUR

"LEST WE FORGET"

We were talking about the passing of Robert T. Lincoln. My friend was a distinguished Englishman. Naturally, the talk drifted to Abraham Lincoln.

CHAPTER TWENTY-FOUR
"LEST WE FORGET"

I

"I WONDER if you realize how criminally untrustworthy your people are in their appraisement of your men of distinction," he remarked.

"More so than are your own people, for example?" I asked.

"Yes, I think so. We are faulty," he granted. "But your contemporary opinion is so cock-sure, as you call it. You permit a personal rancor and virulence to enter into your appraisals. You employ no reserve. Therefore you have farther to go back, more to retract, when you discover you are wrong, as almost invariably history proves you to be."

"You have a specific instance in mind?" I ventured.

"Well," he replied, "take Lincoln, whom we were discussing. He had his faults, but he was hardly an imbecile, would you say?"

"An imbecile?" I echoed.

"That was what you freely and very generally called him. You discussed impeaching him on the score of unfidelity and imbecility, did you not? You called him an 'unutterable calamity.'"

I was silent.

II

"Let us see," said this careful Englishman, and he took down a scrap-book from a library shelf. "One of your distinguished authors and Republicans seems to reflect the prevailing opinion pretty well. Writing from Washington under date of March 9, 1863, he says:

The most striking thing is the absence of personal loyalty to the President. It does not exist. He has no admirers, no enthusiastic supporters, none to bet on his head. If a Republican convention were to be held to-morrow, he would not get the vote of a State. He does not act or talk or feel like the ruler of a great empire in a great crisis. This is felt by all, and has got down through all the layers of society. It has a disastrous effect on all departments and classes of officials as well as on the public. . . . He has a kind of shrewdness and common sense, mother-wit and slip-shod, low-levelled honesty that made him a good Western jury lawyer. But he is *an unutterable calamity* to us where he is.

"Here is what our distinguished jurist, Edward Dicey, saw in America and wrote in his 'Six Months in the Federal States' (1863):

With regard to the President himself, everybody spoke with an almost brutal frankness. Politically at that time Abraham Lincoln was regarded as a failure. . . . When you have called the President "honest Abe Lincoln" according to the favorite phrase of the American press, you have

said a great deal doubtless; but you have said *all* that can
be said in his favor. He works hard, and does little; and
unites a painful sense of responsibility to a still more painful sense, perhaps, that his work is too great for him to
grapple with. (p. 218) . . . The truth is that when the
President leaves the White House, he will be no more
regretted, though more respected, than Mr. Buchanan.
When Wendell Philips described him as a "first-rate second-
rate man" he uttered one of those epigrammatic sarcasms
which stick to their victim forever.

III

"Charles Sumner was certainly one of your great
statesmen. This is what he wrote to John Bright,
August 5, 1862: 'I wish that the Cabinet was more
harmonious and the President had less his inertia':
and on September 18, 1864, he wrote in deploring
Lincoln's renomination:

If he (Mr. Lincoln) had patriotically withdrawn . . . I
was very sure the nominee would be elected. You understand that there is a strong feeling among those who have
seen Mr. Lincoln in the way of business that he lacks practical talent for his important place. It is thought that there
should be more readiness, and also more capacity for
government. . . . Chase for a long time hesitated in the
support of Mr. Lincoln; he did not think him competent. . . .
By the way, I have often observed that Mr. Lincoln re-
sembles Louis XVI more than any other ruler in history.

"One of your distinguished Senators, Nesmith of
Oregon, spoke thus in Congress, February 4, 1863,

of 'the imbecility and inefficiency at the head of the Government.'

"George Ticknor was another of your men of distinction. Hear what he wrote, March 8, 1863: 'It seems to be settled in the minds of the community that a civil war of the gigantic proportions to which this one has attained is to be carried on by the old machinery of party. . . . Why, you might as well get the men and women, and the newspapers, and the caucuses and clubs to put out a volcano or step on an earthquake. If the President don't see this and make a clean sweep, he cannot, I think, get on much farther.'

"Richard Henry Dana, again and as late as May 4, 1864, speaks of people 'fearing that his weak points may wreck him or wreck something.'

"Another of your Senators, Grimes of Iowa, January 14, 1862, complaining in Congress of the President's failure to consult with people, said: 'When, for the first time in six months, I attempted to approach the footstool of the power enthroned at the other end of the avenue, I was told that the President was engaged.'

IV

"Here is a member of Lincoln's own Cabinet, Salmon P. Chase, after serving with Lincoln in his Cabinet for over three years, who wrote, September

17, 1864, that Lincoln 'is not at all demonstrative, either in speech or manner. I feel that I do not know him; and I found no act on what he says or does.'

"Joel Parker wrote, November 1, 1862: 'The President is not only a monarch, but he is an absolute, irresponsible, uncontrollable Government, a perfect military despotism.'

"Senator Collamer of Vermont, on February 11, 1863, said in Congress:

We are appealed to to let our conscience and our discernment go and obey the dictates pressed upon us. If it has come to this that it is to be more than intimated that we are not to consult our understandings, not to indulge in any reasoning about a matter, but we are to be told ex cathedra by the organ of the Administration that the Cabinet desires and all are in favor of a certain thing, as an argument to induce us to cave in, it seems to me that implies a degree of subserviency that can hardly be expected.

"The abuse in the Senate finally became so virulent that Senator Sherman of Ohio, on February 5, 1863, called a halt by saying: 'We do no good to our cause, no good to our country by a constant crimination of the President by arraigning him here as I have heard him arraigned as a tyrant and an imbecile.'

V

"Your press was equally virulent—and wrong," continued my friend. "Take one of your leading

Republican papers, the New York *Evening Post*, and its tone, to my mind, was deplorable.

"On July 7, 1862, this paper commented that the President 'has taken the advice of politicians rather than listen to the beatings of the great heart of the people,' and on August 1, 1862, it wrote: 'God grant that the President may fling off the evil influence of corrupt politicians.'

VI

"Again here is the same paper, under date of March 24, 1863, calling the Administration imbecile:

Every journal in New York arraigned Mr. Lincoln and his Cabinet for an inadequate perception of the duties of the occasion. Mr. Lincoln was allowed to be honest and sincere, but he was too good-natured; he meant well, but he did not act with sufficient energy. . . . As for Mr. Seward, the most cautious and conservative of the Secretaries as he had come to be considered, he was an idealist, a compromiser, a false prophet of good things to come and utterly unable to comprehend either the magnitude or the malignity of the conflict. In the same spirit, Secretary Welles was declared "an old granny"; and the only man of the Cabinet who awoke any enthusiasm and hope was Secretary Stanton. . . . The Administration is weak, it is imbecile, it is unequal to the demands of the crisis, it does not guide but follows at a long distance the indications of public sentiment, it wants pluck and decision, and it must be shoved on by the people before it will undertake decisive measures. Such was the criticism of the leading journals as well as of private conversation.

VII

"On another day, September 15 following, *The Evening Post* said:

It is universally seen that our signal failures hitherto have grown out of a want of policy. It may be doubted indeed whether we have had a government which properly answered to the name of a government. A more or less active machine answering the purposes of an executive agent we have had unquestionably. Some parts of that instrument also have operated admirably; but as a whole it has been deficient in directing mind and has not fulfilled the wishes of the people. The President is universally said to be honest, his devotion to the best interests of the country cannot be doubted . . . and yet the effect of his management has been such that with all his personal popularity, in spite of the general confidence in his good intentions and in spite of the ability and energy of several of his advisers, a large part of the nation is utterly discouraged and despondent. . . . All this has grown out of the weakness and vacillation of the Administration which itself has grown out of Mr. Lincoln's own want of decision and purpose. . . . No such thing as a combined unitary deliberate administration exists. The President's brave willingness to take all responsibility has quite neutralized the idea of a conjoint responsibility. Orders of the highest importance are issued and movements commanded which Cabinet officers learn of as other people do or what is worse which the Cabinet officers disapprove and protest against.

The right and duty of the President to take all final responsibility cannot be questioned; he is made responsible by the Constitution and will be held responsible by the people, but if he would command the confidence of the community, he must commit the general conduct, as well as the details of his administration, to distinguished and competent advisers. No one man is equal to all the tasks that laid upon the Executive of this vast Nation; he must have assistants; he must consult intimately with those assistants. . . . A new Cabinet, provided it contained men of eminent energy, might go a great way to restore public confidence; but of what use their energy, if their conjoint decisions are not to be regarded as the law of the Administration?

"On July 7, 1863, *The Post* again went to the attack: 'His whole administration has been marked by a certain tone of languor and want of earnestness'; on July 18, it criticised him for his 'cautious habits' and lack of 'instant bold decision in great public emergencies when the life of the Nation is at stake'; and it wrote, August 1, 1862:

What is the Administration thinking about? We speak of it collectively because it is collectively responsible, though its members differ greatly in their mental and moral qualities. If there be any member of this Government in perplexity what to do let them resign. . . . This is a time to speak plainly. We do not mean to be sacrificed by the infidelity or incapacity of any of our rulers if we can prevent it. We want boldness, decision, vigor. Irresolution may do us as much mischief as infidelity. . . . The Administration has been dreaming, sleeping, playing, trifling.

"All of which led the New York *Herald*, on March 9, 1863, to suggest that the President might be impeached because of 'inability to discharge his duties.'

VIII

"Have I made my point, at least with regard to Lincoln?" asked my English friend.

"Yes," I conceded. "They are not pleasant judgments to look back upon. But am I wrong in recalling that the same general opinion of Lincoln existed here in England, culminating in *Punch's* famous cartoon of apology on behalf of the English people when Lincoln was shot?"

This time my friend was silent.

CHAPTER TWENTY-FIVE
THE MAKING OF A CARILLON

A carillon had meant little to me except as a word. But as carillons are becoming popular in the United States I determined to find out their genesis: see where they were made, how they are fashioned, and of what they were made.

One morning in our mail we received an invitation from the famous bell-makers, John Taylor & Son, one of the two bell-makers in the world, at Loughborough, England, asking us to come and look at the most wonderful bells they had ever made. So we went.

CHAPTER TWENTY-FIVE
THE MAKING OF A CARILLON

I

No one can exactly imagine otherwise how vital, how personalized a bit of alloy can become until you have seen it take life. Just as a new-born baby does, do you believe utterly that a bell has a soul; that physically and spiritually it is one of the highest realizations of perfect rhythm, alive.

You stand outside the factory, in a small crooked street, lined with those featureless brick cottages selvedging the pavement which are the average of any North-of-England manufacturing town. You know Loughborough is old despite its look of Victorian industrialism. It is of Saxon origin and has its local history threaded with Norman and Cromwellian wars, and, very splendidly for this small place, an honor roll of 477 men whose names are recorded in the striking memorial tower to the late war, where we heard the town carillon played by Ferd Timmermans, the Rotterdam carillonteur. But once you pass through that small incidental factory door, so entirely English it might lead to a laboratory where the atom was being exploded, or an old man making a doll's house—you come into so strange a world. You stand blinking as if you were suddenly shot out of time and space, and for the moment yourself become a bell, hung aloft, suspended above any ordinary: breathless and confused as if something in you were turning itself up for a great peal of the senses in which imagination or memory have no prelude.

The foundry itself is ordinary to the eye, but its whole instinct is so right. Its whitish, softly discolored walls, its high raftered ceiling, its floor of grounded charcoal, these are firm looking, practical, but apart from the sterile efficiency of any sheer factory. Everything marks the craftsman, things have taken on a beauty through use, and a poetry through tradition of use. The floor is of charcoal, because every scrap of metal in the melting is salvaged, and charcoal leaves the alloy clean.

There is no confusion, despite the centuries that clash together on the floor about you. It all looks so homely, so unpretending, so unadvertised, and sure of itself. Here beside you is one chance bell, waiting to be recast. It is "Santa Anna," the date marked 1450. It comes from Wales. In a separate room (or cave, or cell) you keep hesitating on your word there, for the mind tintinnabulates between magic, mysticism, and modernism, according as you look at the giant tenor of Saint Peter's bell called "Big Peter" as it is being recast for York Cathedral, or a small peal made for a Belgium monastery. But it's a world of

bells, bells, bells, above, about, beside you, bells. Poe
would have been stupefied by the most marvellous
world of bells he dared not dream, and they are so
splendidly real, so solid in the rhythm and poise, such
counterblasts of the world's present political chaos,
always rocking Europe.

And all about, moving slowly, with deliberation
always, and with no jar of affected hurry, are the
foundry men. You understand that casting bells
isn't at all a business when you see these men who
have been bred in the service of the bells. It is a rite
—a sacred, mystic rite, and its priestly glow is in
their eyes. Often I watched a workman pause and
lay his hand on a bell. The affection, the respect of
that gesture!

You remember the legend that Fra Angelico painted
his Madonna kneeling before the canvas in his cell.
No one at Loughborough would say so, but I knew
that something in the men I watched around me was
on its knees in the presence of their creature and
creator, for they have been created by the bells, as
the bells have made their men.

The actual history of the Taylor foundry goes back
to 1370, though young Mr. Taylor is only the fifth
generation of actual Taylor descent in the founding,
and in each generation the secret of the peculiar alloy
is transmitted from father to son, or to the one appointed to carry on. He alone, of all men living,

knows the idiom of the Loughborough bells. It is never written, told only by word of mouth, and told only when dying, or resigning in some way the casting of the bells. Mr. Edmund Taylor, the present head of the firm, is unmarried, and three of the splendid nephews who were here forming their lives for the service of the bells were killed in the war. The last loss snapped off the father, but still there remained one son to carry on, and so he will keep the bells of Loughborough ringing round the world when Mr. Edmund Taylor gives the secret. So that's the thing you feel in everything about you in the foundry, a mystic pervading sense, homely, staunch, yet apart from any other—these realizations were like the very smell of the place, which will always haunt some part of my brain, with its detail of sulphur and molten copper.

And Mr. Edmund Taylor. He is a tenor bell. So calm, so sincere, so instinct with the unobtrusive strength of the men of the North. The man is indeed a living bell, and when he speaks you feel under the carnal observations all the semi-notes of utter simplicity, but dynamic force if called into swing.

Standing now at the factory I was glad to recall some of the things Mr. William Starmer had told me at dinner. He is the greatest authority in England, indeed they say in the world, on bells. He is the lecturer on campanology at the Birmingham University and at Rotterdam. His enthusiasm and his knowledge open another door to this strange world of rhythmic life—bells, their lives continuous with man's own, their religions, art, music, and political history. He gives talks on the wireless on carillons.

When some one mentioned to Mr. Taylor that it is believed that the Liberty Bell was cast at Loughborough, you saw how little advertisement meant to him. He only smiled and said: "I don't like to think one of our bells ever cracked."

Now here we were assembled in the factory, and here was a peal to be cast. Mr. Taylor took us first down into the cellar where a carillon lay in embryo —one thousand pounds of Rio Tinto copper, mined in Spain and smelted into brick-size ingots at Swansea. Each lozenge of tin was stamped with the lamb and banner, just as from early Cornish centuries. From this lamb, Mr. Taylor's house takes its personal crest.

So little fuss, such negligible confusion lay in the foundry where we all assembled for the casting of the peal you could scarcely believe so important an event was taking place. Every one was so sure of the certain thing he had to do, and it was all so personal. How stupid the bustling inefficiency of modern factories will always seem after this.

Only 6 men were connected with the actual casting. They came into a line, three on either side of the oven. The oven itself was so far invisible, being bricked plumb with the wall. But into it two days ago were cast 5 tons of the secret copper and tin alloy—enough to make a peal of 13 bells. Then the furnace was sealed up. A fire (of coal) was lit at seven o'clock this morning, and the metal has wrestled and grappled with its contending alloys until the heat of the fiery furnace (1,100 degrees centigrade) had fused all particles. Now at 2.30 the moment of their birth had come. A hush gripped us. There was no chance expression on Mr. Taylor's face, only his eyes watched everything. Never once did I see him give the slightest direction. Never was one needed.

For there was old Smith now taking his place at the head of the line, for all the world like some strange primeval character, peering forward with a long willow bough in his hand. Old Smith is *the* character of the factory. He is simply a bell. The last human trace vanished at such a moment. James Smith is 67 years old, and has lived his whole life just here with the bells. They all speak so very little, but there was a ring to his voice when he said: "I recast Great Paul (the tenor of St. Paul's, London) in 1881." That is the largest bell in England. Old Smith has the small spare body, the even-featured face so usual here in the North. His whitish beard only accented a face such as Conrad loved. The casual, usual, but master of crisis such as this. . . . In a small sort-of-pulpit, a foreman directed, very quietly, some minor opera-

tions as to the swinging of the ladle and some prelimi-
naries. Then old Smith stepped forward. Two men
knocked out a brick from the oven. Old Smith with
the absolute mystic, dignified air of a priest at some
primitive rite, seized his long willow wand and in-
serted it, stirring the molten copper. Willow, of all
wood, is chosen because it smoulders but does not
burn.

Afterward when I asked Smith why, he said: "I
think *they* like it." Already in the furnace the bells
were personal for Smith.

Now he churned the burning copper, then scummed
a bit, then "Ready Lads," and the men were forward.
Each with a rhythmic gesture of accustomed understanding stood by while the turret swung into place.
The metal is also tested with a pyrometer, but Smith
is believed infallible.

First a spout connects with a large iron ladle (like
a huge gypsy pot). Into this the sparkling scarlet
mass flows, all evenly, its own concentration seemingly
intense as the men's, for the slightest disturbance of
the formula may mean a whole recasting.

"Steady, steady." Smith attends every move, his
bright small eye directing more than his voice, which
is hushed to a whisper.

First a small ladle is quickly filled from the larger
one. This metal is immediately cast into five small
moulds for treble bells. These moulds all stand on the

floor about a few inches in the charcoal, and have been black-leaded, so when they cool the new bell is left clean. The metal is first poured into the shank, or small pot, and I see the men carry it forward between 2 forked iron handles. Treble bells are cast first because then the metal at first heat seems thinner.

Now, quietly and quickly, old Smith, his great willow wand gesturing and prodding the lively scarlet mass, directs the swaying crane, and with a "steady, steady" it pours into the tenor and secondary moulds. There is scarcely one drop too much. The moulds clamped into the charcoal floor receive their precious pregnancy as if they knew their privilege and the melody and rhythm which they, like a mother, were to cast out. A little cloud of white froth lay on the metal as it was poured into the last bell, and I thought: "It is the caul that lies on the face of those born blessed."

Now in the silence, in the constant sense of rhythmic motion, you see the men and bells are one, for as after a bell has rung its notes, still it retains generically a poise in its very shape. As if it were proud of essential economy in the fine masterful way, so I watched the faces of the men as they seemed to reckon. "Not a drop too much, not a drop spilt." It was well done. Now they are back at the furnace. Two men are forward, with iron rods, which they cross one over another to take the weight of the big rake as they rake out every particle of the remaining metal which is salvaged down to a penny size.

The big bells may be taken out in 24 hours, the smaller bell according to size leave their moulds.

Big tenor bells take two months to cast. Then comes the slow process of tuning. A tenor bell is tuned 20 times. Again in the tuning foundry I watched the men as well as the bells. They seemed to do so much more by instinct, so much more by far than any machinery, even that which they use for shaving off the tiny particles out of tune. Each bell contains 5 partial tones. Each must be not only self tuned, but in tune with one another. Some Belgian chimes had come over, not made here, but sent to be recast. As we struck them they sounded tinny, like a goat bleat after the beautiful full, ecstatic tones of the Loughborough bells.

More goes into the tenor bell. For that is the consolidation of an old mediæval ceremony when a bell was indeed the soul of a community given tongue. Indeed, Mr. Starmer told me the casting of a tenor bell goes back to the very primitive days when it was born secretly.

A tenor bell is cast only at midnight. In utter silence, in the solemn hush of that appointed hour, in the mystic spirit of the older men, who used to fast the whole day before its casting, a tenor bell comes from the womb of the fiery furnace and has the breath of life breathed into it, at midnight in this foundry.

In older days, it was the custom of the monarch or lord who gave a bell to send something of his own to be cast in it—some gold ring, or signet, or key. This was a universal custom in the Netherlands until about 100 years ago.

So one sees how we were reborn in the understanding of a bell as Loughborough understands it. Not only must the carillon be in tune, the hearer must be in tune with the carillon.

So we felt that evening as in the perfect moonlit beauty of the fields these people gathered round to hear their carillon. The bells have been their life, their history. Men's and women's faces lifted as they chimed "Lead, Kindly Light"; for the bells of Loughborough, given in war memorial, had told these mothers, fathers, and children what they had told their men fallen: "He who seeks to save his life must lose it." Mr. Taylor has given the tenor bell in memory of his three nephews fallen.

CHAPTER TWENTY-SIX
THE LONG AND SHORT OF IT

I was now ready, after five months, to turn my face homeward. For no matter how informing and broadening are one's visitations to other lands, the differences in living and people make poignant a craving for familiar scenes and cherished friendships.

CHAPTER TWENTY-SIX
THE LONG AND SHORT OF IT

I

IT is worth getting back to the United States if only for the ease with which one can find a good hotel. For it is passing strange that with the number of American tourists in England, willing to pay for the best, the hotels outside of London should consistently remain so uncomfortable and badly kept.

The English are slow to change, and that is their privilege. But is it too much to ask that their hotels "in the provinces" should bear some resemblance to ordinary sanitary regulations, to cleanliness, and to comfort? But go where you will: the more superbly beautiful the place where one longs to linger, the worse the hotel. For other than in Liverpool, Bournemouth, Grassmere, Broadway, Tumbridge Wells, and Bath, we found not a modern hotel with either accommodations or food even inviting or palatable. Baths, private with rooms, are still universally frowned upon—an attitude which places England far behind France in comfort of travel. The inns are clearly impossible for even ordinarily careful folk.

It is difficult to understand this year-after-year refusal of the English to introduce comfort and good cooking into their provincial hotels. And yet everywhere we heard grumblings because the American tourists remained in London and spent their money there, the grumblers being seemingly oblivious of the truth, even when it was explained to them, that people naturally remain where, at the end of a tired day of travel or sight-seeing, they will find the comfort of a good room, the refreshment of a bath, and the enjoyment of a well-cooked meal.

II

I am entirely willing to believe Henry Ryecroft when he says that there was a time when it was a joy to eat English bread and that a justly steamed English potato was an achievement of culinary art. But it is no longer true. If there ever was a lightness and sweetness to a slice of English bread it has gone: everywhere one travels in England the bread is heavy, soggy, and tasteless. An English-done potato is the same: soggy and watery. The Irish can and do still bake or boil a potato that makes the mouth water, but the English have lost the art. The same is true of English-cooked meats, except a shoulder of Southdown mutton and roast beef. But the steak has lost its flavor. If James I were to return to-day he would search in vain for a loin of beef such as that which led him to draw his sword and knight the steak before him as Sir Loin, and thus create the sirloin steak. Many

have smiled at a King giving knighthood to a loin
of beef, but it is hardly any more strange than con-
ferring knighthood on a bridge, as was done not long
ago on the bridge at Bideford. No, the English have
lost the art of cooking. Eggs might as well be strangers
to them for all they know about how to turn an ome-
let, or poach or scramble an egg. Fish they still boil
and grill and fry deliciously. Vegetables are rarely
appetizingly done. This is all the more strange because English vegetables are, owing to the climate,
among the best in the world. The ever-present cabbage is sometimes deliciously done. Good butter is
prevalent everywhere in England, but the English
will themselves confess, if you press them, that seven-
eighths of the butter served in England comes from
the Netherlands and Denmark, and, as a matter of
fact, so does a very large percentage of the eggs on
English tables. In the line of sweets, England's tarts
and puddings are still supreme, but it would be wiser
to leave her present attempts at pastries to the French
and ice-cream to the Americans. Besides, in a climate
such as that of England ice-cream can never have a
profitable place. Coffee in England is atrocious, but
this is made up by the delicious cup of tea which you
can get in the most dilapidated English inn—an
institution, by the way, which has also degenerated
and is now best read about than stopped at.

The trouble is that English cooking is to-day without a principle. Good cooking is no longer the gospel that it used to be. What England needs to-day is a chain of cooking-schools where ordinary good cooking would be taught and the English supremacy of the kitchen regained. A perfect loaf of bread, baked not of white but of whole-wheat flour, might well be to-day the remaking of England in more ways than one.

III

There is no doubt but that a stay of several months in England, with one's understanding in a receptive state, convinces one that England is by no means "down and out." In point of fact, this wrong conception becomes daily, as one meets the people, increasingly ridiculous. England's problems are undoubtedly many and complex. But her tenacity to overcome them is proverbial, and that marvellous faculty of the English to "muddle through" is strong in her people. Her elderly generation is pessimistic: calamitously so. Talk with the men who have been, and one begins to wonder whether there is hope. But I was particular to look for and analyze the generation that is coming into activity, those who were ten to fifteen years of age during the Great War, and are now from eighteen to twenty-three years old. They are a fine type: these young Englishmen, and they are beginning for the first time to take hold of things.

They are more progressive in their ideas than the older generation, and they may give English conservatism a jolt or two when they begin to be heard from. But that will be well for the Empire. The English must be jolted out of their George the Third period ideas and notions. There will be a clash between the ideas of the young and old in England in the years to come. London is already beginning to show what will soon be the prevailing condition all through England. Her buildings are changing, and while many of us may deplore what we call the "atmosphere" of old London, the truth cannot be avoided that a more appropriate word for that "atmosphere" is soot and a sombreness that does not reflect modern ideas. The London of twenty years hence will not be the London of to-day, but, by the same token, the England of 1947 will not be, in its perplexities, the England of 1927. These young Englishmen are girding their loins, and while they will be respectful of the history of their land, they do not intend, as I gathered from talking with many of them, that an adherence to the obsolete customs of the past shall impede present and future progress. There is, in the minds of these sterling young chaps, a greater England. But it will be a different England.

IV

There is a quality in the English that is very difficult, even to the most discerning, to understand: the
place that the human and its sorrows and sufferings
has in the heart of the Briton—compared, for example,
with his feeling for other interests. I know he locks
himself up tight: his feelings are never on his coat-
sleeve. He has the most marvellous control of his
emotions. But no one acquainted with him can venture to say they are not there. Yet, there are char-
acteristics, or call them indications, that are very
difficult to understand.

We were stopping with friends in a small English
town when the cow of a neighbor gave birth to twin
calves. Half the population turned out within the next
few days, and brought the mother-cow carrots and
turnips with expressions of sympathy that were very
touching. Then, the wife of the farmer who owned the
mother-cow duplicated the feat of the cow. She had
twins. Not a woman in that village called upon the
human mother! There were no carrots and turnips
for her!

One of the most tender and kind-hearted English
women I know would, on a cold night, light and place
a kerosene lamp on each side of a potted geranium
plant to protect it from freezing. Yet, when a neighbor lost her fourth son from the effects of the War,

she would not call and offer her condolences. "I do not know her," was her explanation, and go she would not.

A pet peacock one day went to where peacocks go after life, and the family at "The Manor" talked of nothing else. So did all the tenantry. For three days while we were there the calamity was discussed when the bird was buried with the most solemn honors. A mother in one of the tenant-houses, a few days afterward, lost her only baby. Not a soul went near her, and she laid away her baby with her husband—all alone!

I am the last to say that the English are heartless. I have had occasion to read their hearts in the few times when they have permitted the inspection. But such incidents as these—and there are many others —make very difficult a true estimate of a great people.

Is it that the Briton has become immune to human suffering? As Rudyard Kipling once said: "The Briton has at least this advantage over the American: he is hundreds of years ahead in suffering—and sufferings of all kinds."

V

I cannot leave the English without telling a delightful story, told by Sir James Barrie himself in fact, of the first night when Barrie's one-act play *Shall We Join the Ladies?* was produced in London.

The author was in one box, while the Prince of
Wales was in an adjoining loge. But the presence
of Sir James was unknown to His Royal Highness.
As soon as the curtain dropped on the play, the
Prince's remark was plainly heard by the author:
"Well, that's that. Now what is the next damned
thing I have to go and see?"

They tell, too, those who were on the inside, that
when Sir James was asked how he thought the evening had gone off he said: "Quite well. But don't
you think it would have been better if my playlet
had been the only one?" Whereas, John Galsworthy,
whose play *Loyalties* was given on the same evening,
remarked to a friend who asked him if he was satisfied with the production of his play: "Yes, although
I really think that if Barrie's play had been given on
a separate evening, it would really have been better
for both of us."

So, the humanities reach to the top!

VI

We had scarcely got ourselves comfortably adjusted to our steamer-chairs and finished an absorbing two-volume book when we were told that the
following day we should set foot on the soil of that
quiet city on the East River where noises were not,
where simple little hotels had 2,000 rooms and 2,000
baths, where the Smiths were and the Cohens are,

and where the newspapers are ever "bright"—and always accurate!

And before many days the quiet of the Devonshire moors and the gorgeousness of the Cornwall coast were all mixed up with the canyons of New York, and the thousands of struggling moles who ride in the subways of the great empire city of the United States!

VII

I was in New York scarcely twenty-four hours before I was made to feel thoroughly at home. I was watching the driving of some excavation piles for the foundation of a large building when the foreman, seeing my watchfulness, commented: "Interesting, isn't it?"

"Very," I replied.

"How many piles do you suppose we are driving in that hole?" he asked.

"Can't imagine," I said.

"Two thousand, eight hundred," he informed me with pride. "The largest number ever used in connection with a single building in the world."

Always "the world"! Never anything smaller!

"So?" I queried.

I recalled the thrill I had, only two weeks before, when I realized that the Royal Palace at Amsterdam in the Netherlands rested upon 13,659 piles, and was told of the hundreds of thousands of piles upon which the entire city of Amsterdam was built decades and decades ago!

But I was once more in the nation where the world is bounded by the Atlantic Ocean at one end and the Pacific Ocean at the other!

VIII

But I also saw this—and, of all places, in Wall Street.

It was between two and three o'clock, when the afternoon traffic in the narrow financial artery was at its height. A constant stream of automobiles could scarcely make headway, when suddenly midway between Broadway and Exchange Place chauffeurs and drivers held out their right hands and the traffic stopped, and a ten-foot lane across the street, from curb to curb, opened. The automobiles in the rear began to toot their horns, but the chauffeurs in the front on both sides merely turned and smiled at their impatient brethren. The semaphore distinctly signalled "Go," but go the lane of cars would not. The drivers merely looked down and smiled. The sidewalks now became choked with men and women, and they smiled! The windows of the buildings became filled with smiling faces. Everybody was looking at the suddenly parted lane which led from curb to curb. Traffic police now pushed their way through, with determined faces, to break up the crowds, but when

they reached the lane their faces took on a softer look
—and they smiled.

All stock quotations and financial deals were forgotten. Men, hatless, with letters in their hands,
messengers, coatless, with stock-slips in their hands
—all stopped, and all were a-smile.

And at what?

A mother-cat had led her two kittens to the edge
of the curb. Then, taking one of the kittens firmly
in her mouth, she looked around for a moment and,
with measured tread, started to cross densely-traf-
ficked Wall Street. When she reached the middle of
the street, she deposited her charge on the asphalt,
went back to the curb, seized the other kitten and
deposited that one next to the first. Then, sitting on
her haunches, she looked at the two for a moment to
catch her breath. With quiet resumption, she once
more seized the first kitten in her mouth, took it to
the other curb and deposited it until she went back
to the other, sitting serenely in the middle of the
street, and brought it to the curb. Then the three
sat on their haunches and looked at each other. Simul-
taneously, every automobile broke out with a chorus
of honks, from the sidewalks and the windows came
volley after volley of applause, while the mother-cat,
with her two kittens, looking neither to the right nor
left, marshalled beside her, disappeared in the door-
way of an office building. With faces wreathed in

smiles, employer and clerk resumed his and her work. The police gave the signal for the automobiles, now reaching for blocks, to proceed.

While thousands went to their homes that evening to tell how motherhood had completely paralyzed traffic in the busiest street in the greatest metropolis in the Union.

And I like to think that *is* America!

IX

Yet I cannot help a reversion of thought: How *does* Mr. Hwfa Kenwood pronounce his first name? And when, on his holidays, he went to Wales and climbed Tvoedrhwfuwch Mountain and took a punting trip down the Wchwfdrh River—how did he tell his friends where he had been?

Or, worse still, how did he orally tell people when he stopped for a week in the town of Llanfairpwllgwyn-gyllgogerychwyrndrobwllllandysiliogogogoch?

Of course, Mr. Kenwood might retort and ask how do you tell your friends when you have met your American citizen: Kalani Kanmehamehakahikikalan-ynakawahinekuhao?

PART III

CHAPTER TWENTY-SEVEN

I SUPPLEMENT MY DOCTOR

After two months of the quiet hour before dinner which my doctor had recommended, with a session of the 'dropped jaw," I found that I was not getting on top of my indigestion as I hoped. It may well be that it takes a longer time to repair nervous damage than we have the patience to give. My physician, I felt, had started me on the right road. "But, after all," he had counselled, "you can do more for yourself than I can." Accordingly I determined to try.

CHAPTER TWENTY-SEVEN
I SUPPLEMENT MY DOCTOR

I

I was scarcely home twenty-four hours when my friend and physician ran in. A quick look, and his greeting was: "Well, you do look fit. You're a new man."

"That's the way I feel," I returned with a smile. Then, I couldn't resist the disclosure.

II

Before I left for Europe, I had a series of X-ray pictures taken of my stomach from every angle. When the operator had developed them, I told him I had the pictures taken of my volition, and would he explain them to me. He showed me that the opening of my duodenum tube was smaller than is usually the case. That fact I carried with me. It was the only thing wrong with me, he explained. But what *was* the duodenum tube? I had never heard of it. What was it there for? These were the first things to find out, and I did. Now, if the opening of the duodenum tube was contracted, it naturally followed that solid foods could not go through it. These foods, therefore, must remain in the stomach longer than if the outlet were normal, and this, I figured, must cause putrefication and discomfort! So far, so good! But which were solid foods? Meat, of course. Well, why not give up meat? My happiness was not dependent on meat. I liked a steak or a filet. But I could be happy without it.

It brought to mind the attitude of Colonel Roosevelt when his physician ordered a radical change of diet. The doctor warned him it would be radical. "Do what you consider best," answered the Colonel. "I have no habits that I cannot correct: and no ideas that I cannot control."

It was this same physician, Doctor John H. Richards, who wanted to apply a mustard plaster to Colonel Roosevelt's chest, but was warned by Mrs. Roosevelt that her husband had a decided aversion to outward applications of all kinds.

"How about it, Colonel?" asked the physician.

"Doctor," was the reply, "you may put a mustard plaster on my chest: one on my back: I will sit on one, and, if you wish it, then I will eat all three."

III

But what in the place of meat? I never cared much for vegetables, so the idea of being a vegetarian did not appeal strongly! What were the substitutes for meat?

The sea foods and dairy foods? I got a table of food-values, and it was not long before I figured out that I could really get as many calories, high vitamin content, proteins, iron, and all the other valuable food elements in the sea foods and dairy foods as in the animal foods—as a matter of fact, more. Besides, I had never been quite able to thoroughly convince myself that the human was ever intended to eat the carcasses of dead animals. So I made up my mind to shake hands with Mr. Armour and Mr. Swift, and see what a parting of patronage with the goods which those gentlemen provided would do. I might cling to a rasher of bacon, a chicken croquette, occasionally a sausage. But otherwise, meats and fowls and I were to be strangers. So I tried out my new thought.

IV

Now on this particular morning after my return I thought I would casually bring up the subject of a non-meat diet to The Man of Medicine—not as applied to myself, but as a general proposition.

"Not for you," he quickly assured me. "Not for a single moment. You are in good shape now. Now let well enough alone. It would be distinctly wrong."

"Why?" I asked.

"You would lose vitality, weight, and strength," he said.

It was a mean advantage to take, but I couldn't resist it.

"Think so?" I ventured.

"Know so," he returned. "You must eat meat in order to have strength."

"But I thought that meat doesn't give strength?" I asked.

"What does it give then?" he came back.

"Energy," I returned. "Energy which is burned out within two to five hours, dependent on the kind of meat." I had been reading up, was ready for him, but after I had quoted two or three of his own pet authorities, one his own book, he scurried to the two other losses which I would sustain.

"You would show it in a loss of vitality and weight," he countered.

"In how long a time, for instance?" I asked.

"Oh, a week, a fortnight: that depends: certainly in a month," he assured me.

"See any loss of vitality in me now?" I inquired.

"Of course not, but you go on a meatless diet and it would soon be noticeable," he argued.

"Let's go and weigh," I said, and on my scales I showed I had gained eleven pounds. "That's eleven pounds in six months," I commented. "Remember the last time?" He did.

"Well, my dear fellow," I told him, "I haven't eaten meat of any kind in six months!"

V

It *was* atrocious!

But he was a good sport.

"How's the pain?" he asked.

"Not a pain in five months," I wickedly told him.

He came back well. "All right," he said. "How did you work it out?"

"With your table of food-values and a book or two, including your own," I assured him.

He laughed. "I give up," he said. "It's a bully experiment, I'll say that. I haven't seen you look so well in months. Let's have some pictures taken, however," he ended, evidently not entirely convinced.

I did. But twenty-four hours before I did, I ate some meat. The pictures showed the meat as still in the stomach, causing the first pain I had for a half year.

"You win," said The Man of Medicine.

VI

While I was abroad, following my non-meat experiment, a friend said, when I told him of it: "That's interesting. Let me give you a book that bears on that subject." He gave me a book called *How to Be Useful and Happy from 60 to 90*, written by a prominent English physician. I forget his name, for some one borrowed the book and, having the usual faulty memory that book-borrowers have, failed to return it.

I had not gone far into the book before I came across a personal experience which the physician-author had with one of his patients, and which my friend had in mind as bearing on my non-meat experiment. This patient, a woman, came to consult this doctor with regard to some organic trouble, and upon making an examination he was amazed to find her body literally covered with bruises. Upon inquiring the cause, the woman was stolidly silent and refused to give any information. It was only upon her third visit that the physician won the woman's confidence to extract from her, upon discovering newly made bruises, the information that the bruises came from almost regular daily beating inflicted upon her by her husband. She explained that her husband was a man of an uncontrollable temper, and there was scarcely a day when she was not the victim of his outbreaks. From her gentle disposition, the physician soon concluded that these beatings were not the result of any cause given by the wife. Finally he asked her if her husband ate much meat. "Regularly three times a day," was her answer. He counselled her to gradually eliminate meat from one of his meals, giving the high cost as a reason and their inability to afford it. Not much change was noticeable until she began to cut meat out of his daily second meal, and when she had restricted meat to a single meal per day the change in the fiery disposition of the husband was distinctly noticeable.

The doctor then had a talk with the man, and found him to be the opposite of the type of husband whose joy seems to be the beating of a woman. He explained the experiment which had been made upon him by his wife at the physician's suggestion. Immediately he suggested that he refrain from all meats. This was done. It is now four years since the man has eaten meat, except occasionally, and a more exemplary husband can hardly be imaginable. The case was publicly reported by the physician, using of course no names, and the experiment has been tried numerous times by English physicians not as applied to wife-beaters, but with men and women inclined to irritability, and always with signal success.

Here, surely, is real food for thought for wives who may be troubled with husbands of irritable temperament!

CHAPTER TWENTY-EIGHT

RETIREMENT REACTIONS

Upon my return I found an accumulated mail, the size of which appalled me. I had asked that no mail be forwarded, and had postponed the employment of a secretary. That need now was clearly evident.

CHAPTER TWENTY-EIGHT
RETIREMENT REACTIONS

I

WHEN a man retires from business, it evidently connotes to a large part of the public that he has accumulated vast wealth, and I was amused and interested how many there are who were anxious to tell him how to spend it. Likewise another number who want to make it easy for him to employ his leisure.

My retirement was no sooner announced in the newspapers than the deluge began—from every part of the country and from all kinds of people.

II

I soon learned that every one who makes an appeal to those whose names they see in the newspapers and whom they think have the means to financially contribute to public uses sincerely believes that his or her letter is the only one received by such persons. Where the impression is closer to the facts, then the conviction is expressed that, while there may be other worthy causes, the particular purpose for which a contribution is asked outranks, as a "crying need," all those others, this ground being taken without any actual knowledge of what those others are or may be. Each particular proposition is "the most important," "the most vital" or "the most pressing" need of America to-day, and usually it is pointed out—with a singular disregard for brevity—that unless this particular idea is carried out the hope for America's ultimate survival is indeed slim. There is no questioning the sincerity of these writers or the worthiness of many of the objects. Where the mistake lies is in the naïve assumption that his or her request is the only one, or in the thoughtlessness of the simple fact that one can give wisely just as much and so far, and that scores of projects, worthy of themselves, do not come within the plans of his giving or the scope of his most pressing interests. That a person, whatever his willingness to help, may have reached his mental or financial saturation-point is never taken into consideration. "I don't doubt you are helping much and widely," these letters concede, "but let me bring to your attention," and then comes "the most crying need of to-day" or "the most vital question before the American people of modern times." These worthy people really think they have a copyright on these phrases, and that they are distinctly their own, whereas not a single letter comes but contains the same exclusive classification, the same "crying need," and the same warning note as to America's certain disintegration unless this particular cause is supported.

III

I may serve these worthy folk if I give them some idea of the requests which come in an endless stream, each day varying only in the character of the requests and amounts. And pray remember that my case is, in a large measure, obscure. Let me take the last five months' mail which I found awaiting me, and give not a full list, but just the "high spots" in this deluge of requests:

A Memorial Hospital.......................$1,000,000
A Denominational College Endowment........ 1,500,000
An Endowed Magazine...................... 500,000
A Collection of Old Books and Portfolios...... 100,000
A Hall of Fame on Pacific Coast.............. 1,000,000
A Calvin Coolidge Junior Boys' Home........ 1,000,000
11 Farm and Home Mortgages. Aggregating... 170,000
A Correct Speech School.................... 500,000
A Theological University Endowment......... 1,000,000
A Purification Drama League................ 500,000
A Community Sport Stadium................ 500,000
8 Awards Aggregating...................... 400,000
An International Peace Society.............. 1,000,000
A U. S. A. Free University.................. 1,000,000
An International Language College........... 500,000
A Travelling American Student Organization... 250,000
81 requests for individual financial assistance
    of all kinds: musical, medical, dramatic, and
    collegiate students: loans to widows: capi-

tal to begin all kinds of shops, tea-rooms:
help for invalids: ranging from $250 to
$10,000: etc., etc.........................   140,000

114 requests. Totaling....................$11,060,000

This was for five months. Now double these figures
and add two months, and you have a total of close to
twenty-five million dollars in one year!

Nor does this take into account any of the several
hundred indefinite appeals "leaving the amount to
your generosity": nor is there included personal so-
licitations or overtures made through every conceiv-
able channel of acquaintance, friend, or family!

I do not for one moment criticize these folk for
asking: the depth of their sincerity would alone make
such an unkindness impossible. I merely recite the
facts so that the hundreds of unfavorable answers
which must inevitably be sent may, perhaps, be more
clearly understood—answers which are equally unpleasant for the writer to send as they are for the
recipient to receive.

IV

No one who receives letters from young people can
fail to be impressed with the urgent need for a new
universal conception of success. As a matter of fact,
this word has been pretty badly manhandled. Take
ten young men, and nine associate the word only

with money. If a man has made a fortune, he is a success: if he hasn't, he isn't. If he reaches a commanding position, he is a success: if he doesn't, he isn't. The affirmative is, of course, true, but the negative is not, although, as the witty writer has said, "all generalizations are false, including this one." It is only natural that in an age of so much crass materialism, we should have gotten far removed from the actual derivation of the word which plainly tells us that success means that which comes after: a result: an outcome: some favorable termination of something attempted. Now a result or an outcome of something attempted may consist of happiness, and we do not have to be so very old to realize that happiness does not necessarily mean money. In fact, where the latter is, the former is more often than not completely absent. Once a word gets a positive association, however, in the public mind, it is difficult, almost impossible, to change its meaning or uproot it from its unfortunate soil. In the mind of the young to-day success spells wealth or position and very little else. It is idle to say that this is an American interpretation. It is world-wide. I wonder whether those who write would not serve their fellows if they gave the word success a rest for a while, and substituted the lesser-used word achieve. To achieve is to carry something to a finish (a characteristic that is by no means as natural as it should be in America). It is to perform something: to accomplish what one sets out to do: to get something or somewhere by an effort: to win: to attain: to fulfil: to execute. To achieve does not necessarily mean to accomplish some material end: a thing achieved may be by valor, by courage, the result of some praiseworthy effort. It seems to me we would come closer to the actual meaning of the old Latin word successus if we approached it by way of achieve. Above all, we would get a bit farther away from the present deep-rooted and single misconception of success.

V

One may ask "Is a word so important?" Very. Particularly to the young mind, which is naturally very apt to continue the thought of his elders. It fixes achievement wrongly in his mind as applying only to a result spelled in money or position. Consider how few out of a thousand can measure up to such a definition. Then, how about the many? Are they, conversely, not successes? Are they failures? Is the skilled, conscientious country doctor, as an example, whose name is blessed in a community, whose ministrations reach out far and wide beyond his place of abode, whose skill is at the asking of the sick in all kinds of weather and at all times of the night—is he to be rated a failure? Is the other figure in every community, the man of God, conscientious of duty, a failure because his salary is small and his name is not known beyond a range of ten miles? Are the farmer, the merchant, the lawyer, honest in their dealings, with their actions based on immovable principles of impeccable honor—are they failures? Is success to be only conceded to those upon whom God has bestowed ten talents, and failure accorded the man who was given four, or six or eight talents, and uses those to the limit of greatest usefulness? We do not realize how uncomfortable a place this world would be to live in if we all had been given ten talents, and proved ourselves leaders! Successful leadership is only possible to the few, and their achievement is only made possible by effective support, and that means the conscientious followers who have a lesser number of talents. Leadership without a following would be a pretty futile thing. The history of the world is full of the records of men who achieved in the ranks and never became leaders. But what would the leadership have amounted to, what would it have achieved, except for these men? The gold star may never have been theirs, but they are not the only worthy ones without a star. Because a man's name does not blaze forth in the newspapers does not mean that he is lacking in achievement. As a matter of fact, the world to-day is being actually benefitted not so much by its brilliant leaders, of which there are so few, as it is by the hundreds of men of plain sense who by the exercise of that God-bestowed gift influence men and women around them.

So a word *is* important: mightily so when it has come to the point where its absence as applied to a man makes of him one who has lacked of achievement. This country is full of men and women who have achieved: who have lived fully and deeply, and who in the truest sense of the word are successes, and who as means and position are measured nowadays have neither. What these men and women have, however, is the respect of their fellow men, because what they have done has come from the greatest thing that man can possess: character. And their works have been born of that precious possession. They may leave behind them only thousands, counted in dollars, where other men leave millions. But what they do leave behind them is the record of a life of character with their actions born of truth. More than that no man can leave behind. Upon the lives and records of such men is a really great nation built: not upon its millionaires.

VI

Lying before me now is a letter right along this line of thinking. It is from a young man, ambitious to do the right thing. He asks:

"What constitutes a well-lived life, a life of which one can truly say that it is a success?" That is a hard question to answer. The nearest that one can come to it is that a really successful life is a life of truth, spoken and acted: of fair-dealing, which means honesty and kindness, and of charity, which means consideration for others. The Golden Rule, in other words. Sounds simple. And it is—provided you have the character to live it. Then, in proportion as to the number of talents given you, to carry on and through such a life, will you be known of men: some by many, some by few. The number is immaterial so far as achievement goes. We achieve, we succeed, in proportion as we are given opportunity and place. To some it is given to touch thousands of lives: to others only a few. But the achievement is there in both cases. Sometimes the influence is more intensive where the circle is small: the achievement actually greater. Many a man of ten talents has been awakened and developed by a man of five talents. The scholar often becomes greater than the teacher. But is the work of the teacher thereby made less effective: his achievement less great? Is he less successful than the soul which he has awakened and which goes to a greater work in a greater circle? Some inspire. Others do. Without the inspiration, the doing might not have been. Hence the inspirer achieves, or succeeds if you will, as surely and as truly, as the doer. The world only sees the doer. But he who has done knows the true source. The honors of the world go

to the man whom the world sees. It can do naught
else. But many an honor resting on the name of men
the world over would, if truly bestowed, lay on the
bier of some man or woman who was known only to
them and a few others. They worked in a small sphere,
but they achieved. Their work goes on through the
influences which they had on other lives. To say of
such men that they were not successes in the greatest
meaning of that word is the same as to deny the
wreath of success to the mother or wife of a man who
achieves. No man ever achieves except by reason of
another, and, usually, another of whom the world
knows not, but who lived a successful life by reason
of the fruit which its influence bore in another. That
is success: that is achievement: that is a well-lived
life. All else than character and the influence of character matters not.

Other things cease: character goes on.

VII

It should not be possible for such a letter, part of
my morning's mail, to come from an American home,
worthy of the name. A familiarity with domestic
conditions as they unfortunately are in many another home makes one fear, however, that a similar
letter might easily have come from firesides that are
all too many, where parents feel the "call" to solve

problems of others, forgetful of their own responsibilities:

"I am twenty years of age, the third son of a family of four. Our home is of the typical well-to-do sort in a city of the third tier of population. Our means are easy—too easy, I fear. My father stands high in the community as a business man. He is in advertising, and, if my observation is correct from the other advertising men who come to our table, knows little else. His sole other interest is golf, and so the table talk, such as it is, is composed of advertising and golf courses and golf scores. Even mother has confessed that our range of talk is pitifully circumscribed. One-third of the time my father is in New York or Chicago or Detroit or Boston on business. When he is at home he is at his office from nine until six: on Sundays he plays golf. In the evenings when he is at home he has either a "prospect," a customer or some advertising man at dinner, and all evening there is talk of nothing but advertising from every angle. He has scarcely an eye or an ear for any of his four children, and so either we vanish to our rooms or we go out. He does not know where. He is a liberal father: a good father, in a way. But he simply has no time for us. We have a summer home on the Lake, and there, too, is a constant procession of prospects, customers, and advertising men, either as over-night or week-end guests. In other words, father is business: an excellent type, I should say, of the typical American business man.

"Mother is fine, too, just as fine in her way as father is in his. But she has no time for us children either. She is on this Board and on that Committee and Chairman of this and President of that. She is either at a meeting of some sort, writing a report of some kind, or trying to get on top of a large correspondence or her ear is glued to the receiver of the telephone. I cannot but think it ironical in a way that she should be Chairman of the Board of our local Orphan Asylum. I really do not know of four more complete orphans than us kids. Last week I could not help smiling when I read an account of a speech that mother delivered on the education of children! It was a good speech, I will say that for it, for mother is clever. But two of her children couldn't help making a comment or two to each other on the irony of that speech, with mother totally unconscious of it. We have five servants, trained to their work, and so the house runs much of itself, although it must be said that it runs smoothly. That is, there is always enough to eat and the rooms are well looked after. But mother is so busy with her outside work that even if she wanted to give us children more thought and time she simply couldn't do it without her outside interests suffering.

"Now we are in trouble. Dick, the eldest, has

slipped his foot, and is in trouble. I don't know the exact nature of it, because we children all go our separate ways and lead individual lives. But I can guess what has happened. And if sister continues going with the same crowd, in which she is a prominent figure, it won't be long before her foot will slip.

"Father and mother are in sackcloth and ashes over Dick's slip. He is told that he has "brought disgrace to the family name," and all that. Of course, he has. I keep quiet and say nothing, because repression and not expression is the rule in our house. But all the same I can't help doing a little thinking to myself, and I try not to criticise my father and mother and be a disloyal son. But I can't make it out any other way but that father and mother are more to blame than Dick. He is not a vicious kid any more than I am, but are we expected to have the limit of common sense and self-restraint before we are thirty? I don't say this thing might not have happened if father and mother had been a bit more on their jobs. It might despite them. But because they were not, it is as natural as water running down hill to have one's thoughts go along that line. Clem, my youngest brother, thinks so, and said so to me last evening and I was sorry the thought was in his mind. But, after all, is it so unnatural?

"I hate to bother you with all this, and I don't know why I do, because I know you can't help us.

I feel, from reading everything about you that has come my way, as if I could talk to you, and you would understand. I have to talk it out with somebody. I haven't any one else. Father has said that he knows you, and I felt this would give you an understanding of our condition that another might not have. It's a mess, Mr. M——, and the worst of it is that no one is wilfully to blame."

VIII

No, this is not an exceptional letter, as some reader may surmise. I wish it were. I print it here as a type of others which I and others all too frequently receive, unknown to parents: a reflection of what is going on in more families than some of us dream. Only two weeks ago I received a heart-breaking letter from a little girl of fourteen, not complaining, but in the sweetest and most anxious manner telling me of her mother's unconscious neglect of her and the little problems that beset a girl in her teens. This poor child had practically been shuffled off to an aunt of whom she was not fond. I take pains to verify these letters, and in not a single instance yet have I found the conditions exaggerated in these pitiful outcries of the young. Are such conditions brought about by the absorption of fathers in business and mothers in interests outside of their homes? If so, we are indeed riding for a fall!

IX

Speaking of young people:

A father wrote me about a year ago saying that his young lad of eleven was not "humping along" as his father wished he might. His home was that of plenty. The father had done everything he could: the mother likewise. But the boy continued to be slow. Everything was an effort: the slightest difficulty was an insurmountable difficulty. He was timid, shy. Boys with less to do with mastered tasks which this boy could not grasp. He had no perseverance. The father asked if I would talk to the boy: a fresh voice, he felt, would help, and so forth—the all too usual parental failure to grasp a child. I had a talk with the boy. That was a year ago. Yesterday he came to see me. The boy was transformed. Not because of what I said to him, but what he had done for himself. I had suggested the Boy Scouts to him. The father was lukewarm about the idea. The mother had the notion, wrongly harbored by so many mothers, that the Boy Scouts savored of militarism: she didn't want to bring her boy up to be a soldier and the usual misconception of this remarkable boy organization. But the boy had become aroused to the idea and had his way. He became a Scout.

"Things look a bit easier to you now?" I asked.

"They certainly do," was the smiling answer.

Then, with a radiant face, he went on: "You know that part of the Scout law which says that you should smile and whistle when a difficulty comes along?"

I did.

"Well," said the boy, "when I am up against a thing that needs a bit of bucking up, I just smile and whistle and I say to myself, 'Just watch me do that little thing.' And I do it. You must have thought me a chump a year ago."

There is food for thought in this little incident for many parents who find that there is good raw material in their child, but somehow or other the right way to arouse and direct it seems to elude them. I hold no proof for the Boy Scouts except that I know what it did for both of my boys and what its rules and laws can do to awaken many another boy whose parents need their conception of the Boy Scouts set right!

CHAPTER TWENTY-NINE

WHEN AUTHORS TALK TOGETHER

"As you are writing a book," said a friend the other day, "and going to become an author, why not let me include you in an invitation for dinner with a group of your brothers-to-be? You will meet some eight or ten authors in an informal way."

I accepted.

CHAPTER TWENTY-NINE
WHEN AUTHORS TALK TOGETHER

I

My first contact with authors was exceedingly fortunate. There were some eleven authors dining in an informal way at a round table—a group which came together three times a year "to compare notes." I had read the books of these men, but had never seen them, and it was interesting to compare the men with their work. On the whole, there were no illusions shattered.

II

The talk was very free, full of interesting observations and anecdote. One member of the group had just returned from a visit to Kipling at his Burwash house, and told of discussing a certain American writer.

"I haven't noticed anything of his for some time," said Kipling.

"No, he's not writing: he's studying," Kipling was told.

"Oh," was the comment. "What's he studying?"
"Style."

"Style?" echoed Kipling. "Oh, Lord, then all *is* lost!"

III

The talk turned on misused words when one of the authors in the group mentioned that he had that day spent an amusing hour looking over a dozen floral catalogues, noticing how cleverly and differently each avoids the use of the word "magenta" in the color descriptions. "Take the Azalia Mollis, for instance," he said, "which, as every one who has ever planted it knows, is a screaming magenta. But in the catalogues it is anything but magenta in color. It is 'a beautiful purplish red' or 'a red suffused with purple' or 'a dark-toned red' or 'a dull-toned scarlet.' Other flowers of the magenta variety are described as:

> rosy mauve
> lovely violet pink
> crimson blended purple
> ruby-purplish
> rich ruby violet
> soft rose violet
> rich old rose with blush of violet
> pinkish-mauve

"Anything but the truthful word 'magenta.'

IV

"I don't suppose that any color represents so much brain-power to describe it by some other than its real name. Of course, nurserymen know that to use the word 'magenta' is to sound the flower's death-knell, and it is to the credit of American gardeners that this is so. In only one catalogue is the truth even cautiously approached in the suggestion that 'where this variety is planted alone, away from other colors, it makes a distinguished effect.' That is true. I have seen a border of Azalia Mollis with a background of green that was a delight to the eye. The trouble is that there is something about magenta-colored flowers which invariably leads their possessors, as if by magic, to put them next to a blazing red or in front of a red brick wall. Of course, to some gardeners magenta is simply a variety of red. It must be so from the way they will plant the magenta Petunia in a bed with flaming red Geraniums, or next to the scarlet Canna, or the magenta Wichuriana Rose next to a brick wall. I presume the reason we do not like magenta is that it is really not a color at all, but a bastard product, or, as a friend of mine refers to it, a disappointed pink.

V

"If it be true that the word came from the Italian town Magenta, which in turn derived its name from the color of the blood shed there during the battle of 1859, there must have been something physically wrong with the soldiers who could shed magenta blood. At all events, American gardeners are to be

congratulated upon their determination to keep the
tone out of well-kept gardens. It would, too, be to
the credit of American nurserymen if they would
cease in their attempts to mislead new gardeners
by unconsciously introducing the obnoxious tone into
their beds and borders by the use of confusing terms.
Not only could they spare themselves brain-energy,
but horticulture would suffer no loss if the few ma-
genta-toned flowers were entirely eliminated from the
market. In fact, it would be a distinct gain to scores
of gardens."

VI

One author, also an editor, just returning from
England, asked the group if they had—as he had—
forgotten the English bit of rhyme—very old—about
the farmer:

THE
FARMER'S
ARMS

Let the wealthy and great
Roll in splendour and state,
I envy them not I declare it.
I eat my own lamb,
My own chickens and ham,
I shear my own fleece and I wear it.
I have lawns, I have bowers,
I have fruits, I have flowers,
The lark is my Morning alarmer:

> So my jolly boys now
> Here's God speed the plough,
> Long life and success to the farmer.

I had to confess I had never come across it!

VII

Another, at this point, produced a letter from an author to his publisher which he commented upon as one of the cleverest bits of writing of that sort he had ever come across. It seems that Homer Croy went into seclusion to write another book after his *West of the Water Tower* was successful. As nothing resulted from his period of seclusion, his publishers wrote him and asked if he had gotten down to work. He replied that he had not, and gave this as his reason:

"I think I really could get to work if it wasn't for my white pants. The idea of wearing white pants in winter is ruining me. I get up in the morning, have breakfast and then instead of going to work in my bathrobe, I think to myself, 'I'll just put on my white pants, take a stroll for a while, come in and then go to work.' So I put 'em on. After I have strolled a while I think, 'Well, I'll just have lunch first.' I eat. Then I say to myself, 'I'll go out and look at the flowers a few minutes and then go to work.' I look. It is now time for afternoon tea. I have tea. Then I watch the people playing tennis a while, and pretty soon it is time for dinner. So I take off my white pants and put on the black—and another day is gone forever. The next day I put on my white pants and start all over again. If it wasn't for those white pants I could get something done. They are nice pants. I bought them especially for this trip—I simply can't throw 'em away. If I am late with my new novel, don't blame me; put the blame where it belongs—on the pants."

VIII

The talk now turned to the accusation that the most successful authors of to-day sell their art for a mess of pottage. That there is foundation for this sort of talk was not denied by this group. The moment an author publishes a successful book, his is the invariable experience that he receives a deluge of offers for a second book—always from those publishers or editors who had nothing to do with his success, and would have withheld a chance from him six months before. Some authors, flushed with success, succumb, and become the victims of these "best-seller" hunters. That is how a "one-book author" is made. The first book is written with care and art, and ample time is taken to produce the best of which the author is capable. Then comes the author's acid test: whether he will be influenced by the offers, meaningless other than the large amounts involved, or whether he will repeat the process of his first book. There are those who pursue the latter plan, and they join the ranks of Kipling, Galsworthy, Conrad, and the others who cannot be persuaded by the tuft-hunters. They will not compromise art for money.

IX

The story was then told of a successful author who recently refused an offer from a magazine for 12 articles for $20,000. He did not like the ownership of the magazine, and he sold the same articles elsewhere for one-half that sum. His action was the more creditable because he has a wife and three children, and the money would have come in handy. A novelist present then told of an acquaintance of his who not long ago refused $40,000 for the magazine rights to his new novel because he could not approve of the standards of the magazine. He sold the rights to the same novel to another magazine for $25,000. "Fifteen thousand dollars less," he explained to his friend. "But I have preserved my self-respect and held on to a principle." His means are moderate, too. The work of another writer was discussed—an author's work that is greatly in demand. He has written two books: both successful. But he was wise enough not to key his living expenses to his new success, which is the real secret of why a number of our reputable authors have made associations creditable neither to their reputations nor their art. It got into the newspapers that he was writing a third book, and the offers began to come in from the magazines. He has two daughters to educate: was anxious to take his family abroad for six months, and some of the offers looked very good to him. But he considered their source, and finally accepted the one next to the lowest offer. But he picked a magazine where he would be read not for his name, but for what he had to say. Two other authors also came up for discussion. Both are among the popular writers of the day, who became intoxicated with their success and the money into which it could be translated in certain quarters. They sold their art for a mess of pottage, because, foolishly, they had allowed their economic expenses to creep up on them, and then the battle with the pen was on. They have both changed their mode of living, and thereby reduced their expenses, and have gone to live in the country where what they write will represent their art at its best and not savor of "pot-boilers."

I got the impression from all the talk that it is indeed a wise child, in the world of authorship, who knows its own father!

And fortunately for literature some of the children of the pen, from what I heard, are beginning to take notice that there is something more to life and living than the flesh-pots of New York!

X

A very good piece of writing on a much-discussed subject came into the discussion. It was produced and read by a business writer present.

"Do I believe in Luck?" wrote this man. "I should say I do! It's a wonderful force! I have watched the successful careers of too many lucky men to doubt its existence and its efficacy.

"It is this way:

"You see some fellow reach out and grab an opportunity that the other fellows standing around had not realized was there. Having grabbed it, he hangs on to it with a grip that makes the jaws of a bulldog seem like a fairy touch. He calls into play his breath of Vision. He sees the possibilities of the situation, and has the Ambition to desire them, and the Courage to tackle them. He intensifies his strong points, bolsters his weak ones, cultivates those personal qualities that cause other men to trust him and to co-operate with him. He sows the seeds of sunshine, of good cheer, of optimism, of unstinted kindness. He gives freely of what he has, both spiritual and physical things. He thinks a little straighter; works a little harder and a little longer; travels on his nerve and his enthusiasm; he gives such service as his best efforts permit. Keeps his head cool—his feet warm —his mind busy. He doesn't worry over trifles. Plans his work ahead, then sticks to it—rain or shine. He talks and acts like a winner, for he knows in time he will be one.

"And then——

"Luck does all the rest."

XI

An interesting revelation came into the talk when I got to chatting with the author at my right about a new book which I was reading. It was distinctly along his own line of writing, and I assumed, of course, he had read it.

"No," he said, "I haven't read it. I don't read, you know."

"What do you mean by that?" I asked.

"Just what I say," he returned. "I haven't read a book for twenty years, I should say."

"Old or new?" I queried.

"Old or new," he repeated. "I never read, except the newspapers."

XII

An author sitting across the table broke in at this point, and declared that Joseph Conrad followed the same rule.

"One day there came in my mail," said this author,

"a copy of Conrad's *The Arrow of Gold*, with the inscription in it

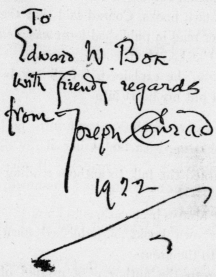

To
Edward W. Bok
with friendly regards
from Joseph Conrad

1922

"I wondered. I did not know Conrad: had never met him. After a while, a mutual friend explained how the book came to me.

"I wrote the author a note of appreciation. Then came an answer: 'I sent *The Arrow of Gold* to you in appreciation of the pleasure you gave me with your latest book. I read it: something I have not done for a long time—read a book.'

"Still I wondered, until I was told that Conrad practically never read a book—'except one,' he said to a friend, '*Jessie's Cook Book*,'—a recipe book by Mrs. Conrad! He was always threatening to read an edition of Henry James which he had on a shelf, but never reached a reading of the first volume.

"Of his own books, Conrad said that the only one he had ever read in published form was *Youth*.

"'Why?' asked the friend.

"'Because,' he explained, 'of all my books, it is the book I put my heart into.'"

XIII

This turned the talk to authors reading their own books.

"I have always been curious to know if you authors read your own books in published form," I said, speaking to the group.

Turning to the author of a myriad of books, I asked: "Do you, may I ask?"

"Why, no," he answered. "It would never occur to me. "Do you?" he asked of the group.

"No," every man returned, except one who confessed: "I glanced over my first one, from a matter of pride, I suppose, but I didn't read it."

The whole question seemed to be summed up by an author of over a dozen books: "I have never heard but one author say that he had read his own books after publication. Why should he? He wrote them."

XIV

"Well," said one author most interestingly, "I make my bread writing books, and I am fond of them. I am not like Conrad. But I do think there is a distinctly limited influence in reading too much. That may sound at odds with current ideas of books. All the same, it is true. A book-worm can be just as cramped as can a musician."

Then he told this instance:

"It was just a blue-skyed, cloudless spring day when, some years ago, I went out for a walk with a friend who had come to spend the week-end with us. This friend was essentially and completely a book-worm. He literally lived in books or in book-stores buying more books. Every foot in his house bulged out with books. I never met any one who had read so much, who could read so fast, and who was always ravenous for the next book. His was a true case of

> 'Insatiate to the spring I fly
> I drink, and yet am ever dry.'

Only his spring was a book. A novel a morning was his diet, with another after dinner, and a book of biography was an easy afternoon's work. Twenty books a week was his steady average. And I will say for him that he remembered what he read. You could scarcely mention a book, modern or classic, he had not read, and if you happened to hit upon one unfamiliar to him he would not rest until he had gone to some library and gotten it. He read as fluently in French as in English, and yet when he went with me to Paris, not a Frenchman could understand him! He reviewed books for several newspapers and reviews, and did it well, and so all the important books naturally came his way.

XV

"This particular afternoon he was just about to curl in an easy chair with a book when I refused to allow it, and politely, but reluctantly I knew, he went out with me into the ravishing warm spring sunshine. I do not think he was aware of either the sunshine or the new fresh green things pushing the winter leaves aside and breaking the moist soil in their effort to reach the air and the sun. All the time he talked of the latest book he had read, and as I had just read it, he was eager to discuss it. Finally I stopped, and so engaged was he in his discussion that he had not missed me until he was fully fifty feet ahead. Then he looked up, saw for the first time that I wasn't there, and looked back to see me standing under a tree and looking back. After a few moments, seeing that I made no move, he retraced his steps and asked 'What's up? What do you see?'

"'Come here, where I am standing,' I answered,

'and look up.' He came, looked, adjusted his glasses, looked again, and asked: 'Look at what?'

"'See nothing?' I asked.

"'Not a damned thing,' he answered, 'and neither do you.'

"'Look here, Decatur,' I returned, 'you have just been raving about the beauty of de Maupassant's style, stressing beauty as the greatest gift of an author and the most wonderful single quality that an author can put into a book.'

"'Yes,' he replied. 'And what's more——'

XVI

"'One moment,' I broke in. 'You go into ecstasies over de Maupassant's beauty of style in a book, and yet you are absolutely insensible to the greatest beauty in the world: the most delicately beautiful thing that God does at this season of the year when He transforms a barren apple-tree such as this was two weeks ago into a perfect bower of white and soft pink, with the blue sky seen through the branches, and completes the picture with a meadow-lark singing its golden notes on a branch ten feet over your head, and you tell me that you see nothing and probably heard nothing. You miss what is far more beautiful in life itself for a beauty of style in a book. How is it possible?'

"'Well,' he answered, 'it *is* pretty,' and the next

moment he was ready to walk off and resume his de Maupassant beauty gospel! An apple-tree in full blossom had meant nothing to him.

"I yield to no man in an admiration of good writing and books. But as between a de Maupassant passage in a book, full of beauty as it is, and God's miracle in an apple-tree in the springtime, well——!"

XVII

One of the writers present was about to embark on a lecturing tour, and he was made the butt of the group.

Finally, he asked of the group their serious opinion of an author's appearance before the public, and one of the company spoke up, and spoke well, I thought.

"I think," said this writer, "that it is one of the most unfortunate happenings in the career of almost any successful author when he permits himself to be influenced by lecture offers and attempts to interpret his books or his ideas on the public platform. Few can do it successfully. James Whitcomb Riley was a notable exception to this rule, but Riley could have made as great a success as an actor as he did as a writer. He had a strong dramatic element in his nature, and no one ever read his poems as Riley could read them.

"I was present when he saw Sargent's portrait of himself for the first time. He looked at it carefully for a few moments and then, turning to me, he asked: 'Do I look like that?'

"I told him I thought it was an excellent portrait.

"'That's the way, then, I look to the public?'

"I acquiesced.

"'Well,' he returned, 'I guess I'll quit.'"

XVIII

The public has a marvellous faculty of making up its own mental portraits of authors whose books it likes, and few there are who can make good with those portraits. Almost invariably, disappointment ensues. Except in rare instances, authors lose far more than they gain by readings from their own works or by appearing on the lecture platform. Because a man is given a certain ability to write, it follows by no means that he is given an equal ability to interpret his work. He may do it to his own satisfaction, but there is always the audience before him who will, in nine cases out of ten, come to a different conclusion.

I have seen a number of authors attempt this hurdle, but few ever cleared it. Of course, this is equally true of successful men in other lines, but the author has the great disadvantage that he has put a concrete thing in the hands of the public, a book, and from what he says in that book and how he says it, it has formed in its own mind an opinion of the author himself—a mental portrait that is in the majority of cases far from the actual man or woman.

The wise authors are those who cannot be induced to come before the public. "Know me through my written work," they say, and they are right. The wrong path is that which leads to the lecture platform.

An author, like a cobbler, is best at his last!

XIX

The talk now drifted to an introduction out of the usual which one of the authors had in mind for his next book, which reminded another writer present of P. G. Wodehouse's dedication of *The Heart of a Goof*:

To
my daughter
LEONORA
without whose never-failing
sympathy and encouragement
this book
would have been finished
in half the time.

XX

If authors failed of successes as public speakers or readers, they certainly were tremendously interesting around a table among themselves.

For the clock now struck 2.00 A. M.

Whereupon a humorous author at the table gave a fitting close to the evening and morning talk:

"What of it if it is 2.00 A. M.?" he laughingly asked, and added:

> "The cow is in the hammock,
>   The cat is in the lake,
>   Baby is in the ash-can.
>   What difference does it make?"

CHAPTER THIRTY
15 MONTHS AFTER

A confession, it is said, is good for the soul. I don't know that what follows in this chapter has been particularly good for my soul. But it has been a satisfaction to put down what I have written. It may be, as it probably is, faulty in its expression. The truth, however, is there.

CHAPTER THIRTY

15 MONTHS AFTER

I

I AM writing fifteen months after my retirement from active business. Now, what have I to show for this year or more of freedom?

Concretely, nothing—save this book, and the value of this one definite result is problematical.

Generally speaking, I have much to show, and therein lies my gain.

If I had listened to my own ego, and followed my own judgment, I should have gone directly from the business which I had made my lifework into some form of service. Some men have done this, and succeeded. But that is because these business men lived broader lives than I did. They, consciously or unconsciously, prepared themselves for a period of service to follow their period of accumulation.

I did not. I completely submerged myself in business. I looked neither to the right nor left. I worked in a rut, and therefore thought in a rut. I believed in concentration as the chief factor in material success, and I concentrated. Correct, as a theory, and also in practice—to a certain extent. But you can overdo anything—excellent though it be in principle. I overdid. It was business with me, morning, noon, and night. I succeeded, in a material way, yes. But I realize now that if I had sensed worlds other than my own, had permitted other interests to stretch the walls of my mind I would have been a more valuable asset to my company and certainly a greater asset to myself.

II

As an example of this very point: Two months ago I attended a meeting of the Board of Directors of my company, and found, under consideration, as it had been for some months, a question practically involving the future of the corporation. The Committee appointed to look into the pros and cons of the matter had reached an impasse. When the matter was explained, I saw at once the way out and on. Not for a moment was this because my mind was any keener than were the minds of the men at the table. But it happened that economic considerations, entirely outside of the immediate realm of our business, were concerned and bore heavily on the question at issue. I realized that a year ago my own view-point would not have included a consideration or a knowledge of these apparently outside questions.

My eyes would have been, as I realized were the

eyes of my co-directors, so close to the grindstone that I could have seen no farther than the hole. Now, I had not only a clearer perspective, but a wider vision. I approached the matter not from the inside out, but from the outside in. The entire question seemed at once clearer not only to myself, but apparently to my associates. My motion for its solution was unanimously adopted, the course charted was followed, and not only was an association involving millions of dollars perfected but, what was infinitely more valuable to the corporation, a broader company policy was adopted based on research and wider sources of information. Yet my company had been known in its immediate line of business as outstandingly progressive. And it was—along its own particular line. But, in knowledge, it had not embraced other lines, and, nowadays, "the world do move."

Singularly enough, I had attended this particular meeting with the avowed intention of resigning from the directorate, so as to make room for a younger man, and at the conclusion of the meeting I stated my purpose.

"No," definitely replied the president. "Not under any circumstances. You have something now that we have not, and we need it."

A rested mind may have contributed to this result: a fresher point of view. But I like to think that it is rather a longer perspective and a clearer vision.

III

Some one will say, apropos of this anecdote: "Ah, you are still connected with your business, then. Can't let go." I am. I could let go, if I chose, and, as I suggested, I was ready to do so at the meeting in question. But there is really no reason for a complete cut-off from what, after all, happens to be my chief source of income, particularly as my participation means an hour or two once a month, with a complete absence of five months at a time. This is hardly an active participation. My thought of retirement from my Board was solely to make room for one of the younger men. I notice one important point, however: I can sit by my former desk with a perfect complacency and satisfaction, with no desire whatever to return to the latter position. I can see, with no regret or longing, my successor at my desk.

As a matter of fact, my year of freedom has in no wise changed my mental attitude toward the admonition of the physician to the active business man to desist from all participation in affairs, to "cut himself entirely off": to drop his affairs "absolutely." There are, of course, extreme instances where such a course is imperative. But these are few. It is one thing to counsel a man who has been active to reduce the pressure: to go slow: to gradually cast off until he feels he can completely cut the Gordian knot.

That sounds and is sensible. But I cannot for the life of me see the wisdom of the instantaneous transformation overnight of an active business man into an eremite. A physician may counsel the mind to stop its work, the body to remain inactive, but how can he say to the spirit that it must cease its restless outlook? I like to question whether it is good either physically or mentally for a man. A complete cessation from his affairs may be wise for a spell, as it has proven in my case. But to say that a man must be remote, abstract, see the world and not touch it: feel the throbbings of its great pulse and remain absolutely impervious to it, does not belong in the realm of sense, to my way of thinking. Indeed, I have known men counselled to inactivity who have become, by reason of that fact, more keen, more penetrating, and more alive to the world because of their repose and remoteness. A man is by no means most productive in penetration when he is in the midst of affairs. In brief, no extreme is ever healthy.

IV

I confess to a great admiration for a doctor-friend of mine who completely fooled me on an occasion, and, I will add, for my good.

"You're tired out," was his verdict. "Your vitality is low, and that can easily become serious with your stomach trouble if you catch the slightest cold in the lower extremities." Then looking around my room, he added: "Now it is very important that for forty-eight hours you keep out of drafts and currents, and currents of air are strongest on the floors. So, I want you to put on a pair of woollen golf stockings, and stick your feet in that drawer of your desk—opening the bottom drawer. "Have your meals served here, if you like. You can work all right (that is what fooled me). But take your feet out of the drawer only when strictly necessary."

There he left me for forty-eight hours. And there I remained. The forty-eight hours lengthened into ninety-six. On the sixth day, light began to dawn on me. Naturally, with my feet stuck in the drawer of my desk I could not get to the office!

When the physician came that evening I complimented him upon his strategy. He merely smiled. "It has worked with much cleverer men than you are. You're holding your own, and I kept you from going to that damned office for a few days, anyhow."

He had!

V

I told the doctor that his remark about holding my own reminded me of a delicious story which William Lyon Phelps told Woodrow Wilson, and which the latter was very fond of telling.

The Yale professor and a friend were walking one

day from New Haven to Bridgeport when, after they had walked an hour, they asked a stranger how many more miles it was to Bridgeport.

"About twelve miles," was the answer.

They walked another hour, and asked another stranger.

"About twelve miles," came the reply.

Another hour, another stranger: the same question, and again: "About twelve miles."

Whereupon the friend turned to Phelps and said: "Never mind, Billy, it isn't getting away from us anyhow. At least, we're holding our own."

VI

It is that "something" to which the President of our company referred which spells my greatest gain in the year of freedom that lies behind me. And as I mingle with my former business associates, I realize that it is exactly this "something" that a number of business men lack and acutely need.

Just as it was all cement with me, so with them it is all finance or manufacture or barter and sale—and, generally speaking, followed along painfully restricted lines.

I am appalled now at the utter lack in our men of affairs of what I have discovered to be essential points of wider knowledge—contacts upon which I placed no value a year ago. Take the international point of view. Not only is it lamentably lacking in our business men, but its absence is made a basis for boastfulness.

"We have enough to do right here with our own problems. My policy is to stick to them, and let the foreigners settle their own problems. We have nothing to do with them." This from one of the leading manufacturers in the United States, spoken only the other day.

It so happens, however, that we have much to do with foreign problems, as we would readily discover if the markets of Europe were closed to us for a year or two.

"All the same," stubbornly added a banker, "the little old U. S. A. is good enough for me. To hell with Europe."

"I am for America first, last, and all the time," said a third, while another added that most stupid of all self-appraisals: "I am a 100 per cent American," forgetting that there is no such person nor could there be, any more than there could be a 100 per cent Englishman or 100 per cent native of any country.

As a matter of fact, no man when he proclaims himself as "a 100 per cent American," has the faintest idea of what he means. It is a glib phrase with no understanding back of it.

VII

Yet I realize that only a short while since I shared and held exactly these unintelligent views.

I had absolutely no use for the World Court, and endeavored—unsuccessfully, it is true—to persuade the two Senators from my State to vote against it. But when in June I personally attended a week's sessions of the World Court at the Hague, saw it function, and talked with men conversant with its results, I realized I had not known what I was talking about. It was like my intelligent (?) opinions about the conduct of the Great War three thousand miles away, and later what I saw first-hand close to the French front.

It was the same with the League of Nations. I had been influenced by Messrs. Lodge and Company to believe that the League was not for us, and boasted of my position. Last September I attended all its sessions open to me at Geneva. My sheer ignorance of the League came home to me daily, and I left not with the question of shall we join the League, but whether we can afford to keep out of it.

It was the difference, in both instances, of unintelligent theory, repeated parrot-like from uninformed opinion, and first-hand knowledge.

VIII

The trouble with our foreign outlook is that it is based on ignorance or prejudice, with the result that the vast majority of Americans have not an international mind. Their prejudices are created for them. We hug the idea that we are sufficient to ourselves— about as narrow an opinion as one can hold. We cherish the notion that as we are the most powerful nation in the world—for the present, please remember —we can do about as we please, and we employ no reserve in our boastful reminder of the fact to the foreigners we meet here or abroad. Express these views as I do here, and one is immediately tagged as un-American, when as a matter of fact an American is a better American just in proportion as a wider and truer horizon is afforded him. I yield to no one in my Americanism, but I recognize in myself a more intelligent and better American because I have been permitted to discover and broaden my previously prejudiced mind and my stupidly narrow point of view. If my year of freedom has done nothing more for me than that, it would be eminently worth while.

IX

But it has done more. It has given me a wider and more tolerant recognition of currents and eddies of whose existence right here at home I was absolutely unaware. I can clearly see now my wife's correct instinct when she bade me to attempt nothing for a year and readjust myself. It was a wife's love that did not give my restricted vision a more justifiable and correct definition. For years, I had eyes and saw not: I had ears and heard not. I had lived in a fortress built of cement. I had dimly realized the existence of other worlds, but of their actuality, their purposes, the relation they had to a full life, I knew absolutely nothing. I had lived a cloistered existence in a throbbing world.

I know better now. That is, I have begun to know. I am still distinctly on the threshold: in the Freshman Class, so to speak. But at least my mind is open, whereas up to this time it has been closed.

I have begun to widen my contacts: so needful to any man who wants to live a full life.

X

I have recently wondered whether we begin to attach sufficient value to contacts in life: whether we know the value that lies in touching life on all sides. We read of a life of achievement, and almost invariably if we read closely we see how valuable were the contacts in that life. Not necessarily contacts with influential people, but those points of contact which make life fuller, more interesting and worth while, which awaken the senses within us to their full possibility. There are thousands who go through life either asleep or only partially awake, simply because they have not come into touch with those persons or factors all around them which would have fully awakened that spark of desire and accomplishment which God has put into all of us. We are likely to think and believe that these favorable contacts are possible only to the favorably situated: "They are not for us," we say: we believe that an environment cannot be overcome, as can a lack of educational advantages, for example. Take a life such as that of Abraham Lincoln, as only one of scores, and we see how futile is such an argument. Certainly no life could be more humble: more secluded: more prescribed—if it had been allowed so to remain. But Lincoln's stepmother constantly saw to it that her son kept himself in touch with the best that their almost barren surroundings afforded. If she put a book in his way, it was always the best book of its particular kind. If an interesting visitor happened to come within her horizon she saw to it that the boy was present to listen. If she went to the nearest village she took the boy with her, and she picked some excuse to bring him into contact with the most interesting man or woman within reach. If there was a meeting at which she felt something would be discussed which would widen the boy's horizon, she made it her business to see that the boy was there.

their picnics and outings and "Father must come."
But Father couldn't come. Why? Business. As between the calls of contractors, builders, and architects
and realty operators, and my wife and daughters, the
former always won out and the latter lost. I did not
realize it then. I was too engrossed to reach the point
where I should have taken an inventory and realized
where I was going. And had I reached such a "stop,
look, and listen" point, I should have probably gone
on and excused the going, as so many men do, on the
lines of the time-worn-out excuse that I was doing it
for my family. An excuse that sounds fine, but, in the
final analysis, is merely a comforting sop to the conscience of a business man. And a wrong one.

XIV

Thank God I was brought to my senses. A little
late, perhaps, was I in coming. Still, it takes a man
almost to the point of fifty-four to make it possible to
see things a bit fuller and clearly. I have at least this
consolation—meagre as it is—that there are men who
do not get to the point where at my age I have
reached, until they are sixty or seventy. Some never
arrive. At least a man of fifty-four is, or should be,
at the prime of life, with his faculties at their best:
with his mind at its clearest. My regret is that I did
not come to my senses five years sooner, when I consider how widened has become my vision in a little

more than a year. However, I have arrived, thanks
be! Now, after these fifteen months of readjustment,
I am ready to give where formerly I have taken.
Offers and suggestions lie thick on my home-desk—
opportunities far outnumbering my ability to cope
with them. I smile now when I think of how I wondered whether my hands and mind would be full if I
pulled out of active business. The problem is not one of
what, but one of which. The road of service lies clear
and straight ahead, and I feel ready to enter upon it.

XV

Glory be, too, I have no more indigestion, I am glad
to be rid of it. I do not feel about this infliction as did
a man of large affairs who went to a diet specialist
and asked if his dyspepsia could be lessened but not
entirely cured.

"Why not cured?" asked the physician.

"Well," said the captain of industry, "that indigestion is like a danger-flag to me, and I have depended on it so long that I am not sure that I want to
do away with it altogether. When it comes I know I
am speeding it up too fast, and I let down. It's
really an asset to me. But I don't want it quite so
badly, because in its present acute state I'm really
fit for nothing. So how about lessening it? I'd feel
surer if I knew it were there to tell me when to put
on the brakes."

XVI

Still, I did confess to an indebtedness to my indigestion. I was brought up in the belief that depression, irritability, crossness, and nerves on edge were flaws in the character. But with the rise and fall of the expressions of flatulence and that "gone" sensation in the stomach, I began to discover that the outward signs of my disposition would rise and fall, too. With pain and discomfort would come depression and an irritable temperament: with a relief from the discomforts the sun had nothing on me when it came to an effulgent radiance! My wife said that the change, so far as she was concerned, was like living with a strange man! So the important discovery came to me that what I once thought were flaws of character were really physical symptoms. That was something. It was a great deal. I could at least explain, with conviction, to my wife, which I have done at every convenient interval, that my character was really 99½ per cent, and that at such times as I showed irritability it was purely a product of physical conditions. When I consider the number of times I explained this, and the minuteness of my explanations, I wonder that I have seemingly failed to achieve that degree of conviction on this point that I should like, and hoped for. But, of course, this may be due to the inability of the feminine mind to grasp great psychological solutions!

"You will make me drop a stitch in a minute," is the only comment I get.

XVII

A further gain has come to me from my year of freedom which, being perhaps more subtle, is thereby more difficult to describe. When I was in business, I frequently woke up to face a day of doubt and anxiety— Once for three months I carried the deficits of a reorganization of my company from daylight hours into the night. At other times large contracts clung to my mind and I awoke with them. Puzzling questions were carried over from one week to another. The motives of men troubled. There was scarcely a morning that did not mean the problems of a day. Was competition fair? How could the other fellow carry on—apparently successful—at prices which scarcely covered the expenses of the article furnished, with no margin for overhead? Was our overhead too large? Was our product too expensively manufactured? I confess that I enjoyed the disentangling of these problems. It represented business to me. But what I did not realize was that to arise, tired, to a day after a night through which the unsettled question was unquestionably carried on my mind, did not tend toward a resiliency of spirit and a rested mind and body.

I awake now to a day with a sense of happy freedom which I have never known. The daily task ahead has become a daily pleasure—I live with more zest and gusto—I feel younger at 54 than I did at 40. I find it necessary to control the impulse to undertake this and enter into that proposition. I have to hold myself back. The blood runs more freely in my veins. My head is clear when I awake; my body is rested. I live every day with enthusiasm: with an exhilaration that I never felt. I am approaching "twice thirty" and find myself planning to reach the third period of "twice thirty." I am in love with life. I want to live right along and serve and achieve. I feel that sense of freedom which, it is said, the bird feels as it wings through space.

XVIII

I am urging no man to do what I have done. What has proven so satisfactory to me might well prove unsatisfying to another. But I do ask the business man who can to stop and ask himself one question, and thresh it out for himself: Will it satisfy him in the end to go on with the material struggle? I know as well as any man the lure of business: the fascination of its problems: the natural desire of one more deal: one more "killing": one more year! And then——!

But, by that yardstick, the "then" never comes. It is always ahead. Never now. It is always jam yesterday, jam to-morrow, but never jam to-day. The same endless chain. The same old merry-go-round

XIX

It doesn't pay.
I know it now.
The time to stop is when the stopping is good.